D0385553

THE ANATOMY OF SLEEP

THE ANATOMY
OF SLEEP

ROCHE LABORATORIES
Division of Hoffmann-LaRoche Inc • Nutley, N. J.

Esperanza F. Sarino, M.D.
PRIVATE LIBRARY
Epatrodito C. Sarino, M.D.

Copyright © Hoffmann-LaRoche Inc. 1966

Library of Congress Catalog Number: 66-17478

THE ANATOMY OF SLEEP

CONTENTS

This book has been prepared as a service to physicians by Roche Laboratories. The material is intended to provide a highly readable and interesting review of our "other daily life"—sleep. Since rest and sleep continue as a strong ally of the physician in many areas of medical practice, it is hoped that this book can become a handy reference for understanding the function and nature of this phenomenon.

Chapter 1

ON THE NATURE OF SLEEP

THE QUESTION ABOUT SLEEP most commonly asked of physicians is, "How can I get more of it?" The harried physician, more plagued by assaults upon his sleep than the general run of men, often wishes that he knew the answer. A proper drug will indeed induce sleep, but it cannot provide the time for it.

Patients rarely complain about sleep, only of its absence. Worries about sleep are as frequent in medical histories as accounts of recalcitrant bowels. If insomnia does not kill, it causes a great deal of misery, may accompany suicidal depression, and is as demanding of investigation as any other symptom. Sleeplessness quickly relieved leaves no terrors behind it compared with prolonged insomnia. The physician is professionally concerned with relations of sleep disturbances, real or fancied, to a variety of conditions in his patients.

Every treatise on hygiene and virtually every bedtime admonition of mother to child implies that sleep is essential to life and health. Everybody "knows" that sleep is the great restorer, assuager of fatigue, "sore labour's bath . . . balm of hurt minds." Who has never known the diffuse pain of sleep denied or the agony of its brutal interruption—the rude shake that arouses, the doctor's night call, the alarm clock that buzzes the clouded senses? If some drug which banished sleep forever were discovered, so that every hour of our lives might be devoted to leisure and good works, it is likely that most of mankind, save for a few incorrigibly industrious eccentrics, would reject it out of hand. To most normal people, sleep is not only a need but a pleasure.

But what use is sleep, how does it refresh us, what damage does its absence inflict, how much sleep do we need, what organic changes occur, what puts us to sleep and wakes us up? We know very little of the reasons why sleep is essential. Physiologically, sleep has been one of the least investigated aspects of human life. The specific functions and processes of sleep are largely taken for granted even by many members of the medical profession. A biologically mysterious function seems commonplace until an effort is made to understand it.

Poetic and magical conjectures about sleep are as ancient as the race. Animistic beliefs held that the soul leaves the body during sleep, wanders the world at will (evidenced by what some call dreams), and wakes us when it returns to its corporeal encasement. This had the sanction of Plato: "In sleep, when the rest of the soul, the rational, gentle and dominant part, slumbers, the beastly and savage part, replete with food and wine, endeavors to sally forth to satisfy its own instincts."

Aristotle taught that sleep results from evaporation of nutritive material and the ascendancy of heated matter. Thus he accounted rather neatly for the somnolence that follows a heavy meal, but Aristotle rarely experimented. His belief that women have fewer teeth than men suggests a distaste for observational methods. It has been remarked that his relations with women must have been of the most amicable sort. ·

Only in recent years have sophisticated research tools begun to yield new and significant data about mechanisms of sleep and wakefulness. It is becoming possible to submit many of the conjectures about sleep to the rigors of scientific method. The work of sleep investigators in this country and abroad is the substance of the present volume. Most of the findings are of personal interest to everyone who sleeps or hopes to, and many are of special interest to physicians who contend with sleep problems in their patients.

Theories of Sleep

It may seem ridiculously obvious that we sleep because we are tired. But the specific triggers that ignite sleep and wake us are not at all obvious. Nor is the function of sleep as obvious, for instance, as the function of the kidneys or heart or digestive tract. And what is "tired"? It is popular, particularly among lugubrious poets, to liken sleep to a little death from which we are reprieved each morning. To the physiologist aware of the rather high rate of functional activity of the body during sleep—we burn about one calorie per minute during sleep—this is sheer nonsense. However, there is no lack of theories about sleep, or of objections to them.

Vascular theories. Sleep was "explained" many centuries ago as a kind of anemia of the brain. Alcmeon, a contemporary of Pythagoras, concluded that blood retreats into the veins and that the partially starved brain goes to sleep. Blood circulates under pressure in a closed elastic system. Blood supply of local tissues may vary in two directions: an excess, resulting in congestion or distention, or a deficiency resulting in ischemia. Blood pressure commonly falls during sleep. So the brain might slumber from partial starvation.

Other theories explain sleep as a kind of brain congestion rather than of anemia. The basal ganglia of the brain may blush with an excess of blood which puts pressure on sensory stations and subdues wakeful impules. Pressure-receptive centers or baroreceptors play a part in affecting levels of consciousness. The carotid sinuses are involved with regulation of blood pressure. These areas at the sides of the neck are held in legendary respect by small boys who believe that awesomely informed antagonists can knock them out by touching the right spot. Medicine men on the island of Bali induce sleep by massaging over the carotid sinus for a couple of minutes. Raising the pressure within the carotid sinus causes animals to fall asleep. Some very sensitive people may faint from slight carotid sinus stimulation caused by turning the head while wearing a tight collar.

When put to the test, vascular theories do not wholly explain why we go to sleep. Pressure receptors are part of exceedingly complex feedback mechanisms. Explanation of sleep as brain anemia has been out of fashion since studies showed that there is generally a slight but significant increase in cerebral blood flow during sleep, and little change in oxygen consumption.

Chemical theories. Is the brain put to sleep by some chemical agent, comparable to a sleeping pill, generated by the body during the day? Is sleep a way of getting rid of "fatigue toxins" or accumulated poisons? Or is sleep necessary to restore some vital substance that the day's work has depleted?

These and other chemical theories of natural sleep have been weighed in the balance and found wanting. It cannot be said that sleep-inducing toxins or stay-awake body chemicals do not exist—only that none has been identified or shown to be primary to the phenomenon of sleep. Perhaps the most interesting specific molecule is carbon dioxide which we exhale with every breath. We have more carbon dioxide in our blood when we sleep than when we are awake. Indeed, it would be possible to predict which persons in a group of people are about to fall asleep, on a basis of their elevated blood carbon dioxide. Sufficient carbon dioxide concentration produces narcosis. But a moderate increase in blood carbon dioxide may be a consequence of sleep "letdown" triggered elsewhere.

The endocrine system, like sleep, has periodicities. Speculation about humoral and hormonal influences on sleep involve the thyroid, pituitary, and adrenal glands, with the pituitary as leader of the orchestra. Theorists have speculated that ebbs and flows of the anterior pituitary may impose dampening effects on the endocrine and nervous systems, conducive to sleep, and release the dampening, conducive to wakefulness. However, removal of the pituitary gland does not result in permanent sleep or wakefulness.

Injections of epinephrine are antagonistic to sleep. Hypothetical "wake producing hormones," or arousal substances, have been attributed to the adrenal glands. The role of the adrenals in mobilizing bodily responses to stresses gives a gloss of respectability to theories that a distended bladder, an alarming noise, or other threat, may awaken a sleeper via adrenal participation.

One of the most striking aspects of newer knowledge is realization that the endocrine and central nervous systems are much more intimately connected than early anatomists realized. There is reason to believe that the brain, a phylogenetically old part of it, secretes

4

hormones, and science fiction writers may toy with the idea that sleep is sort of a secretion of the brain. It now seems likely that nerve fibers in the hypothalamus secrete hormonal or humoral agents which pass into the anterior pituitary to excite or inhibit its cells. The pituitary may be a storage vessel for neurosecretions of the hypothalamus; nervous and endocrine factors are impossible to separate.

However, hypotheses that chemical substances are primary to sleep and wakefulness are returned by scientific juries with a Scotch verdict of "not proved." There are several cogent objections. If sleep were necessary to get rid of "fatigue toxins" or depressive products of metabolism, these agents should vanish during the night and everybody should bound out of bed in the morning in a state of offensive euphoria promised by exuberant mattress manufacturers. This is not the usual case. Moreover, mental and physical tests show that performance is as good if not better just before going to bed, when accumulation of poisons is presumably greatest, than in the morning.

A few studies of Siamese or congenitally conjoined twins with completely shared circulations offer negative evidence. Whatever chemicals are in one twin's circulation are in the other's too. But one twin may doze while the other is feeding. Each has his own sleep rhythm.

One baffling medical observation is an unsolved mystery. It concerns a tropical disease, filariasis, of which the most disfiguring manifestation is grossly swollen limbs or elephantiasis. The causative organism, *Wucheria bancrofti,* is transmitted by mosquitoes. Strangely, the parasite only appears in the peripheral blood of patients when they are asleep, not when they are awake. Many efforts to determine how the parasites discriminate between sleep and wakefulness of the host have failed. Whatever causes sleep seems to cause the filaria to emerge in the peripheral bloodstream. Do the parasites respond to some unknown sleep-stuff in the blood? Filaria seem to know something about sleep that scientists don't.

Neural theories. To turn off an electric light, shut off the cur-

5

rent. Pull a switch. "Circuit-breaking" theories of sleep are analogous. These postulate that weary dendrites of certain nerve cells retract by ameba-like movements, breaking connections with neighboring neurones, disengaging the flow of current or stream of impulses required for staying awake. The theory lacks objective support.

Pavlov's theory of cortical inhibition had many adherents until it became evident that some modification is necessary to fit the facts. Sleep, Pavlov thought, follows inhibition of reflexes. Repeated stimuli cause exhaustion which spreads inhibitions through the cerebral cortex until sleep occurs. But it has become quite clear that the cortex, although a participant, is not the sole mover of sleep and wakefulness rhythms. There is complex interplay with centers below the cortex, in the brain stem, which may be the areas where sleep begins (see Chapter 3).

Many general theories of sleep are more philosophical than physiological. Perhaps the simplest and least testable is that sleep is an "instinct" which prevents us from becoming intoxicated or exhausted. Schopenhauer asserted that the brain "feeds in sleep," but that the will needs no food. Hence the need for sleep is greatest in brainworkers (he considered himself to be one).

An evolutionary theory of sleep enunciated by Nathaniel Kleitman distinguishes two kinds of sleep-wake: "wakefulness of necessity" and "wakefulness of choice," or "advanced wakefulness." Wakefulness of necessity is primitive, innate, a pattern of alertness essential for survival of an organism confronted by many perils. It is a function of primitive subcortical centers which existed before the cerebral cortex began its regal expansion in the course of evolution. In contrast, wakefulness of choice is a function of the civilized cortex, interwoven with primitive wakefulness keyed to survival. The evolution of human consciousness added certain levels to preexisting levels and elevated us above primitive organisms which, their physical needs satisfied, take snatches of dreamless sleep. It may be, Kleitman suggests, that what keeps man awake two-thirds of the time is curiosity. Probably one of the first signs of increasing cerebral activity in infants is the consolidation of several short sleep periods into long night sleep.

6

We are unconscious when we sleep and our personalities are in suspension. Our brilliance, wit, and accomplishments are denied expression. We can never see ourselves asleep. It is unthinkable that the sprawling, vegetating, perhaps snoring sleeper is the real I. Thus it is only human to regard sleep as strange interruption of the waking state in which we are "ourselves" and the image is most satisfying.

But it is just as reasonable to regard wakefulness as an interruption of the sleeping state. Instead of wondering what puts us to sleep, we may wonder what keeps us awake. This is the point of view of many sleep investigators. It has often been suggested that the basic condition of the brain is sleep, from which we must be stirred to wakefulness. The case has been stated by W. V. Cruven:

"Fetal life is a sleeping life, and it is amazing that the fetus continues its sleep even during labor unless aroused by threatened asphyxia. (Freud stated that, in adult life, when we try to go to sleep 'we try to bring about quite similar conditions to intrauterine life.')

"At birth the baby awakes for a short time but, when anoxic and tactile threats have been removed, reverts to sleep. Unlike the fetus, it is now no longer nourished by a kind of perpetual drip-feed through the umbilical vein and it will starve if it sleeps perpetually. It is accordingly awakened at regular intervals by hunger ["wakefulness of necessity"] but as soon as it has fed it is asleep again. This need for regular feeds remains the fundamental cause for waking throughout life. . . . Like the fetus, the very young baby leads mostly a sleeping life.

"The pattern so far, therefore, is quite plain. Sleep is the original and basic state of life. At first it is continuous; but, as development proceeds, this perpetual sleep may be interrupted temporarily by an increasing number of causes which we may term 'arousal stimuli.' Throughout this very early baby life of sleep, wake is but a temporary cessation of the sleeping state. We certainly could not say that the sleep of this period was a temporary cessation of the waking state. . . .

7

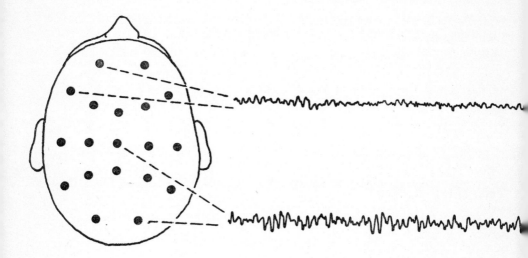

The brain does not emit a single unified rhythm. Frequencies vary constantly and different regions of the cortex give rhythms that vary considerably. Two EEG traces are shown above. Each records changes in electric potential between two electrodes pasted to different regions of the subject's scalp. Modern electroencephalographs employ as many as 32 channels.

"Sleep is always our perpetual background and is 'there' whenever the cause of wake disappears, just as the analogous state of nakedness is 'there' whenever we undress. Even in adult life wake is still a temporary cessation of the basic sleeping state. If wake is a temporary disturbance of the basic state of sleep (and it seems that we must accept this unorthodox view), there is no 'cause' for sleep but only cause for wakefulness."

It seems that arousal stimuli all partake of a threat to well-being, whereas non-waking stimuli are devoid of this threat. When arousal stimuli are supplemented by what Cruden calls "wake maintainers," alertness persists until the waking urge is abolished by satisfaction, fatigue, or adaptation. In this view, common insomnia or unwanted wakefulness is not caused by disorder of the basic sleep state but by wake maintainers which contain a large element of threat, as in anxiety. It may be objected that sleep and wakefulness are two sides of the same coin. Both sides are being examined with equal vigor in current research.

Tools of Investigation

Meaningful studies of sleep had to wait upon an adequate technology, advancing from the primitive electroscope of Galvani to the only-yesterday development of vacuum tube amplifiers. The first brain wave tracings were published some 35 years ago by Hans Berger, a German psychiatrist. They consisted of nothing but wavy lines and excited very little interest. Today, the department of science called electroencephalography—literally, electric writings of the brain—is applied in hundreds of laboratories, both for purposes of medical diagnosis and for studies of nerve functions.

Electrodes taped to the scalp of a subject pick up tiny currents from brain cells near the surface of the skull. The key instrument s an electroencephalograph. Enormously amplified impulses activate inking arms which transcribe electric signals from the brain into wavy lines on a moving sheet of graph paper. Each line is a graph of electric signals from one region of the head. The resulting "brainprint" is called an electroencephalogram or EEG.

The so-called "alpha rhythm" of the brain is associated with sleep and wakefulness. These rhythms have a frequency of 8 to 13 cycles a second—about as fast as you can move a finger. Alpha waves are generally most pronounced when a person is relaxed with eyes closed. They usually disappear when the eyes are open, but may return if a person is extremely bored. As the brain becomes less vigilant, the alpha rhythm slows and disappears. Slow waves with a frequency of 4 to 6 cycles per second appear during sleep. Some people have very faint alpha rhythms. This has no relation to intelligence, but suggests that people have different brain types.

Surface electrodes cannot pick up signals from structures deep within the brain with much success. This handicap is overcome, in animal experimentation, by implanting electrodes into deep-lying brain parts. The electrodes remain in place permanently and are connected as desired to recording devices. The animals carry considerable amounts of hardware in their heads but are perfectly comfortable and live for years. Findings are not distorted by anesthetics, drugs, or surgery. Electrodes have even been implanted in the brains of human subjects and left there for several days during the course of diagnostic workup. The brain does not resent this intrusion of metallic spies and is not at all aware that it is "bugged." Microelectrodes can be inserted with precision into individual cells. Information thus gained helps to identify functional areas of the brain—for instance, sleep-and-wake centers in the brain stem.

Other apparatus records the pulse, eye movements, respiration, gross body movements, and muscle tensions of sleepers. Once a subject's basic sleep pattern is established by such objective methods, many variables can be tested: effects of hypnotic and stimulating drugs, reactions to environment, effects of being deprived of sleep for long periods. Tape recorders register the mumblings of sleep-talkers or deliver standardized stimuli such as a roll of thunder. Quirks of the sleeping mind are to some extent measurable by such techniques.

Falling Asleep and Waking

We do not fall into deeper and deeper sleep during the night until we reach a turning point and become more and more awake. The popular idea that the first sleep of the night is most refreshing, and morning sleep less so, must be reconciled with the fact that we make several fairly sudden shifts from light to deep sleep and vice versa and probably awake several times in the night without remembering a thing about it.

Not very long ago, judgments of depth of sleep depended largely on observations of body movements and intensity of stimuli necessary for arousal. Brain wave evidence is much more specific. American workers designate the various depths of sleep by numbers; European workers prefer letters of the alphabet. Both systems describe the same phenomena. As we fall into uninterrupted sleep, the successive EEG stages appear as follows:

Stage 1. Light sleep begins. The alpha rhythm disappears. Slow waves, 4 to 6 cycles per second, of low voltage (short excursion) appear. Stage 1, returned to after deep sleep, is characteristic of dreaming.

Stage 2. Medium depth sleep. Slower waves, increasing voltages. "Sleep spindles" (short bursts of waves) appear in the pattern.

Stage 3. Deeper sleep. Increasing voltage.

Stage 4. Deepest sleep. Large, slow waves of high voltage.

Having attained deepest sleep, we don't stay there very long. We swing back to Stage 1, probably dream a little, descend again to deeper sleep but may not go all the way. We may pause at Stage 3, or even Stage 2, and return to Stage 1 which is closest to the waking state.

One might think that the brain waves of deepest sleep should be of low voltage, as if driven by a weakened battery, and that the brain waves of light sleep should be of high voltage. The opposite is the case. Electrophysiologists have a ready explanation. In deep sleep, potential builds slowly and clusters of cells fire with a big bang. In light sleep, akin to wakefulness, cells are more "alert," very busy with scanning activities, and their fire-power is more dispersed.

Thousands of EEG "sleep graphs" have been made by investigators, and while there are many variations, the typical or average graph is sufficiently characteristic to warrant some tentative conclusions. In a normal, uninterrupted night's sleep of 7 to 8 hours, we swing from light to deep sleep and back again about 5 times.

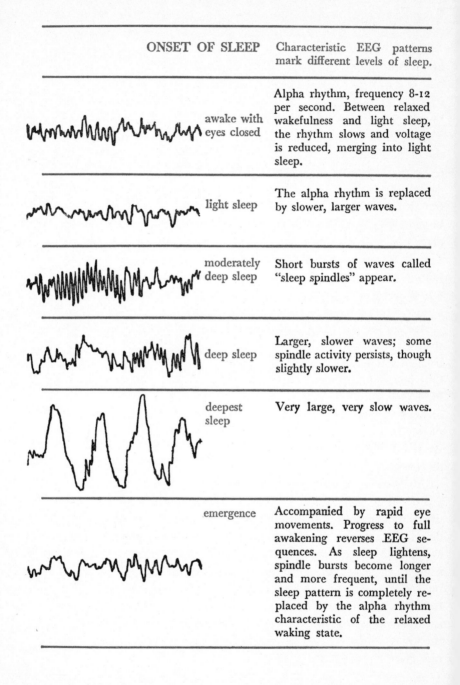

ONSET OF SLEEP — Characteristic EEG patterns mark different levels of sleep.

	awake with eyes closed	Alpha rhythm, frequency 8-12 per second. Between relaxed wakefulness and light sleep, the rhythm slows and voltage is reduced, merging into light sleep.
	light sleep	The alpha rhythm is replaced by slower, larger waves.
	moderately deep sleep	Short bursts of waves called "sleep spindles" appear.
	deep sleep	Larger, slower waves; some spindle activity persists, though slightly slower.
	deepest sleep	Very large, very slow waves.
	emergence	Accompanied by rapid eye movements. Progress to full awakening reverses EEG sequences. As sleep lightens, spindle bursts become longer and more frequent, until the sleep pattern is completely replaced by the alpha rhythm characteristic of the relaxed waking state.

Partial and even complete awakenings occur during the night, although these are rarely remembered unless wakefulness is prolonged.

Here is strong evidence of a basic rest-activity cycle, alternating about every hour and a half. It may also be exhibited through the day in attenuated form. Awake or asleep, we are differently conscious from moment to moment. We are not only sleepy at night, but early in the morning, and less sleepy in the middle of the day. The ritual of the mid-morning and mid-afternoon coffee break, the onset of that tired feeling, the moments when the mind is crystal clear and vigor surges, may reflect fluctuations of a basic rest-activity cycle. Persons with one type of insomnia fall asleep easily but wake after a short time and cannot get back to sleep. It may be that they have anxiety tensions, not necessarily of extreme degree, but sufficient to increase slightly their sensitivity to arousal stimuli at that phase of the sleep cycle—90 minutes or so after falling asleep—when there is a swing back to light sleep and the normal sleeper probably awakens or half awakens but does not remember it because return to sleep is prompt.

Awakening is a piecemeal, not an instantaneous process. No one should feel humiliated, or conclude that his night's rest was poor, because it takes a little while to brush the cobwebs from his mind. One person may awaken more easily than another, but some studies indicate that even when the most powerful, sudden, alarming arousal stimulus is given, it takes 4 to 5 seconds to come completely to one's senses. We are not necessarily indolent slugabeds if we don't leap from the covers with a song on our lips as soon as our eyes open. Hardly anybody does, really.

Spontaneous awakening in the morning is thought to be in part a response to "threat," provoking Kleitman's "wakefulness of necessity." Signals from muscles, a distended bladder, an empty stomach, nag for attention. A forthright answer to the question, "what is the first thing you do in the morning?," is, "urinate." A drowsy state in the morning after awakening is like the drowsiness of falling asleep, and just as natural. There is pleasant drifting between light sleep and wakefulness. The snooze stolen after the alarm clock is turned off is often the most delicious of all, and an early setting of the clock to allow for such indulgence is neither an assault upon morality or physiology.

13

Nobody normally "sleeps like a log." Some twisting and turning is necessary for comfort. Body movements are most numerous during the last half of the night, when sleep is lightest (it cannot be said dogmatically that deep sleep is "better" than light sleep; nature decrees oscillations between the two). If, by reason of deep alcoholic intoxication or other regrettable circumstance, a sleeper remains in one position through the night, the price paid on awakening is usually stiffness, discomfort, even transient paralysis.

It is not uncommon for a body part that has been slept on too long or too hard to protest in the morning. Occasionally, a patient comes to a physician in great alarm, complaining that overnight he has acquired a sore shoulder, a stiff neck, a "dead arm" or a numb leg. In the absence of other causes, the condition is likely to be a pressure neuropathy, resulting from sleeping overlong in a cramped position, producing pressure on certain nerves. Similarly, the symptom of an aching hip may occur in winter. In a cold room, the sleeper tends to hug the warm part of the bed with few excursions into the chilly periphery. This kind of hip ache, which disappears with activity, results not from arthritis but from immobility under a heavy load of blankets.

The Mind at Sleep

There are many stories of people who can set a "mental alarm clock" when they go to bed and awaken at a pre-determined hour. Some of them are true. Studies of a few groups of subjects have shown that some people can awake spontaneously within 30 minutes of a pre-determined time, and a few can awaken precisely on time. Other people do not have this ability. The self-awakeners tended to be more confident of their ability than those who failed.

The mechanism of the internal alarm clock is not known. The clock may be a part of the personal sleep cycle, and practice or necessity may teach the brain to heed it. The brain goes on functioning during sleep, and at a rather high level. Indeed, the sleeping brain is able to make discriminations of such complexity that the cerebral cortex must certainly participate.

Examples of the brain's selective alertness in sleep are common in personal experience. A sleeping mother is awakened by a baby's cry but the sleeping father is not aroused at all (if she jabs him in the shoulder with a demand that he heat the formula, that is another matter). The father, on the other hand, may be awakened by a banging shutter which does not disturb the mother. Somehow, two different brains at sleep come to different conclusions from scanning the same data.

Experiments done at Oxford used a tape recorder to speak a long series of given names into the ears of sleepers. The sleeper's name was randomly dispersed among many others. Subjects were requested to clench a hand when they heard their name spoken. Some sleeping subjects showed a remarkable capacity to respond to their own names by clenching a hand. The experimenters thought that a man might be more stimulated by hearing his name spoken by a woman, and that a woman would be more reactive to a man's voice. It turned out that female voices were more rousing to both men and women. The investigators conjectured that the higher pitch of women's voices gave more penetration. But we might carry an auditory imprint from childhood when mother got us up for school.

What determines the ability of a stimulus to arouse us, in the opinion of many researchers, is its personal significance. In sleep, evidently, our cerebral cortex incessantly sifts out the meaningful from the irrelevant.

Thoughts While Sleeping

The quality of thinking we do while sleeping is not, as a general rule, anything to stir pride in a Phi Beta Kappa. "Thinking," in the conventional sense, is the logical, closely reasoned, integrated, sharp-as-a-tack problem-solving that we accomplish so easily when we are at the peak of consciousness. This is presumably a function of the cerebral cortex. The sleeping brain screens stimuli and burns about the same amount of fuel or oxygen as when solving quadratic equations. Although the cortex functions during sleep, it "behaves" as if it were playful, puzzled, disorganized, and inattentive to principles of straight thinking.

It is unlikely that we think at all in the deeper phases of sleep.

Thinking probably occurs only during the light stage of sleep and in drowsy or "reverie" periods before falling asleep and after awakening. About all of our sleep-thought that we can examine for quality is the tiny fraction of our dreams that we happen to recall briefly (see Chapter 4). Mutterings of sleep-talkers, utterances of sleepy persons, sentences retrieved from dreams and promptly written down, give other evidence of the quality of thinking done when one is drowsy or asleep. On the whole, it is evidence of the most humiliating sort.

Ian Oswald has collected a number of senseless and ludicrous sentences which some call "dream tags," leftovers of thoughts while sleeping. The following are samples:

"The pencil holds well. To the pavement will Tell too."

"They don't want the tickets, they only want elimination of horse."

"And find that all with syphilis is immediately."

"One of the most characteristic features is accelleration of the 16."

"They are exposed to verbally interlection."

"Squawns of medication allow me to ungather."

"Only God and Henry Ford have no umbilical cord."

What is to be made of such prattle? One may speculate that the cortex, as in dreams, achieves triumphs of distortion in blending fragments pulled from the hat of memory along with the shards of all sorts of external and internal stimuli. Elements with little or no relation to each other are put together irrationally. Not a few investigators have remarked upon the similarity of dream phenomena and sleep utterances to schizophrenic behavior. There seems to be a similar splitting-off from the real world and acceptance of the unreal as real.

It would be unfair to blame the impaired organization of thought in light sleep upon the cortex, which evidently does the best it can under circumstances beyond its control. Concentration, integration, problem-solving, "higher thinking" which calls upon experience and learning and consequently the mobilization of memory, is characteristic of wide-awake consciousness with a steady stream of sensations from without and within. In drowsiness and sleep, the

16

cortex is deprived of a great deal of sensory information from the real world. It is, in a sense, blindfolded, and must make do with dribs and drabs of data.

The sleeping brain does its job well, but in many respects it is a different job from the one it performs when awake, and just as important. Seymour Kety has suggested that the tasks of the brain at sleep are quite specialized. In the waking state, we can afford the luxury of paying attention to only a small part of our environment. Things seen from the corner of the eye, approaching footsteps, a burnt odor from the kitchen, a thousand other stimuli, find us ready to take quick action. We can concentrate safely on tasks that promote the world's progress.

But when we are paralyzed by sleep we cannot afford such luxury. Then, Kety suggests, we need to keep all of our channels of awareness open, scanning every bit of incoming information as if one were as important as another. The brain's alertness is more dispersed, more open to recognize danger from any source. Perhaps in sleep there is no such thing as irrelevant information. The brain opens up all its pathways constantly to receive and evaluate input. How else, Kety asks, can we explain a mother's arousal to an infant's cry but not to a slamming door?

Evidently "hard thinking" is superfluous in sleep, and we may regard our ludicrous sleepy utterances with detached amusement. Perhaps organized thinking is a cumulative trauma that must be interrupted by rest. Logical thought seems to be incompatible with sleep. A striking aspect of insomnia is the insomniac's inability to let his mind run down. He cannot, by conscious thought, prevent his thoughts from going round and round in worrisome rehearsal. An hypnotic drug which induces sleep subdues the trauma of unbridled thinking. Twenty-fours of straight thinking may make Jack a dull boy.

Sleepy Body or Sleepy Brain?

It has long been assumed that the brain is central to the processes of sleep. One of the most lyrical passages in all scientific literature is Sir Charles Sherrington's imaginative description of the awakening brain:

"In the great head-end which has been mostly darkness spring up myriads of twinkling stationary lights and myriads of trains of moving lights of many different directions. It is as though activity from one of those local places which continued restless in the darkened main-mass suddenly spread far and wide and invaded all. The great topmost sheet of the mass, that where hardly a light had twinkled or moved, becomes now a sparkling field of rhythmic flashing points with trains of travelling sparks hurrying hither and thither. The brain is waking and with it the mind is returning. It is as if the Milky Way entered upon some cosmic dance. Swiftly the head-mass becomes an enchanted loom where millions of flashing shuttles weave a dissolving pattern, always a meaningful pattern though never an abiding one; a shifting harmony of subpatterns. Now as the waking body rouses, subpatterns of this great harmony of activity stretch down into the unlit tracks of the stalk-piece of the scheme. Strings of flashing and travelling sparks engage the lengths of it. This means that the body is up and rises to meet its waking day."

Here is incomparable poetry and impeccable neurology. Sherrington was one of the world's most eminent neurologists. But descriptions of activities of the brain and other organs merely explain some of the things that happen when we sleep. What is the *why* of it?

Consciousness is the most spectacular phenomenon of life, and its wiping-out is the most spectacular aspect of sleep. It is natural that the bulk of scientific studies of sleep have concentrated on the central nervous system, the focus of consciousness, particularly since its manifestations have become so definitely measurable. Yet it is conceivable that causes for sleep operate elsewhere than in the brain, even though the existence of sleep-inducing centers in the brain stem has been convincingly demonstrated (see page 52). Possibly the tired body takes the reluctant brain along for a forced rest. After all, the brain has nowhere else to go.

Kety has mentioned something of this sort as a speculative possibility: The brain is the servant of the body in sleep. Suppose that the need for sleep does not exist in the brain, but somewhere else in the body—perhaps in the muscular system, the heart, kidneys, or other system. Then what the brain does in succumbing to sleep is what it "should" do in submitting to a resting process.

Is it our muscles, or heart, or kidneys that need sleep? The search for causes and reasons for sleep leads into terra incognita.

The "Cause" of Sleep

It occurs to many people that sleep is like the recharging of a battery that has run down. The simile, in more sophisticated terms, is as popular with scientists as with laymen. Sir John Eccles, moderating a symposium on sleep, remarked: "One can hardly doubt the metabolic basis of the nervous exhaustion, if we may call it so, that progresses over many hours, and which for its elimination requires the recovery process of sleep." He feels that "the exhaustion that necessitates sleep depends upon some progressive running down of cellular activity or cellular responsiveness."

Explanations of how energies drain from body batteries are marked by considerable speculative fogginess—for example, that sleep is caused by "avalanching synaptic fatigue." This might be called the fouled spark plug theory of sleep. It implies that synapses, the infinitesimal gaps between communicating neurones, become dog-tired—or, figuratively, fouled with metabolic wastes—so that sparks cannot jump the gap efficiently, and damping of impulses brings sleep.

But what is fatigue, how does it increase and what overcomes it? Inability to pinpoint the recuperative powers of sleep probably has a simple but tantalizing explanation. The need for sleep, as Sir John Eccles and others intimate, may well be cell-deep. All the cells of the body, rather than particular organs or tissues, may have mechanisms affecting sleep and wakefulness.

Electron microscopes have made ultramicroscopic structures of the cell visible to man, and molecular biology and biochemistry have elucidated many of the intricate processes of cells. But relatively little is known of the microchemistry of brain cells. Ribonucleic acid (RNA) is concerned with the synthesis of protein in cells. Swedish workers have shown that rhythmical changes of RNA occur in nerve cells, that protein content is diminished when the cell is excited, and that cells synthesize new protein in rest periods. Is sleep a pause that refreshes while cells replenish protein? Sleep may be a transient protein deficiency. This could explain how our energies run down during the day and are restored by rest. But it is a view of sleep that requires further investigation.

The mitochondria of cells also are intriguing. These tiny potato-shaped structures have been called "power plants" of the cell, with good reason. Carbohydrates are processed within these cell furnaces to produce energy-packed molecules (adenosine triphosphate or ATP) which are the immediate sources of energy in a form that living organisms can use. Perhaps sleepy mitochondria produce less energy to recharge our batteries, so we feel sleepy all over.

Ultimately, the "cause" of sleep may be found to reside in occult molecular processes of our cells. We may get sleepy when our molecules do.

Do good sleepers live longer than chronic insomniacs? Controlled experiments in human beings are not possible. Nevertheless, the idea has some philosophical and a little evidential support. The life span of man is longer than that of other organisms, with a few exceptions such as sea turtles of indolent disposition.

Raymond Pearl's experiments in the 1930's may have relevance to sleep and length of life. Pearl's studies of fruit flies led him to the conclusion that the rate of living directly affects length of life. He postulated that organisms are endowed with a finite package of vitality, which may be greater or less in individual organisms. The faster they live, the sooner they drain this energy reserve and life comes to an end. Pearl concluded that "in general, the duration of life varies inversely as the rate of energy expenditure during life."

It remains to be proved that a "purpose" of sleep is to prolong one's natural life span, but sleep indubitably does reduce energy expenditure. This may give pause to people who regard sleep as a regrettable waste of one-third of their lives, amounting to years of unconsciousness during which they might better be employed in the energetic pursuit of high achievement. Evidently we should not feel guilty about sleep, but should relax and enjoy it.

Chapter 2

THE
ENIGMATIC NEED

Anyone who has counted the ticks of the clock the whole night through "knows" that sleep is a desperate necessity. It is widely believed that dire things will befall the person too long deprived of sleep, and that extremely prolonged sleeplessness leads to insanity. Intimations of disaster are naturally most pronounced in insomniacs, who suffer most from sleeplessness, and indeed may suffer so acutely that their requests for relief merit the physician's serious attention.

It can be said at once that there are no reliable reports of human deaths caused by sleep deprivation. Impairment of normal, alert, purposive function is another matter. Enforced sleep deprivation is a form of torture, and it has been employed in Russian and Chinese "brainwashing" techniques to extort false confessions of germ warfare and the like. The victim is questioned at night when he is sleepy. There is delay between questioning episodes. The same questions and statements are repeated endlessly while the victim is denied spontaneous activity. Eventually, when the victim is near the breaking point, the inquisitors become friendly. At that time the victim has an impaired grasp of reality, his vigilance is low, his suggestibility high, and he "confesses" to things of which he is innocent.

Alterations of behavior caused by lack of sleep are real enough. Not all such alterations are quite what one would expect. There seems, for instance, to be a limit beyond which we do not become more sleepy, but just more tortured. And if we are sufficiently motivated to perform some task involving a complex challenge, our efficiency may not be impaired at all by loss of 30 consecutive hours or more of sleep. Many studies indicate that sleep is a vital need, without shedding much light on the fundamental nature of this need. In Churchillian phrase, it is an "enigma wrapped in a riddle."

Experiments in Sleep Denied

One way of measuring the effects of lack of sleep is to prevent people from sleeping and see what happens. Numerous laboratory studies of sleep deprivation or "experimental insomnia" (a term to make insomniacs shudder) have been made with benefit of sensitive instrumentation. Watchers keep volunteers awake for days and make continuing observations.

Self-imposed sleeplessness of 24 hours or more, to meet a deadline or finish an important task, is not uncommon. But in such case, the person may actually get snatches of light sleep with his eyes open and casual experience reveals little.

Rarely, a self-imposed incident of sleep deprivation chances to come under scientific scrutiny. Epidemics of ambulant insomnia occurred in the 1930's in that social excrescence known as a "dance marathon," wherein contestants shuffled pitiably around the floor, with occasional time out periods under observation, until all collapsed except the winner. A comparable instance of a man who stayed awake for 168 hours and 33 minutes, a solid week, in a "radio marathon" has been reported by Drs. John T. Brauchi and Louis J. West.

Two participants took alternating 30-minute shifts talking into a microphone, continued without sleep. The contestant who came under medical observation showed abnormal symptoms from the fourth day of sleeplessness onward. He thought that parts of the equipment were in different cities, and suffered memory lapses which were said not to impair his broadcasting performance, a comment of possible interest to sociologists of radio. He could not understand why there were no cars speeding up and down the aisles of the building. He opened a refrigerator door to let a non-existent woman in out of the rain. He accused his girl friend of kissing one of the guards although she was alone in the broadcasting booth with him.

Physicians ended the contest on the seventh night because of the psychotic and physical states of the participants, both of whom developed ankle edema. The contestant who is the subject of the report continued to have memory lapses, thought that a female secret agent in Florida was trying to shanghai him to the Suez Canal zone, was irritable, restless, failed to show up for work, and was troubled by insomnia at night. He entered a Veterans Administration hospital and his medical history revealed that he had had three previous hospitalizations for nervous disorders and that he had previously engaged in a radio marathon that kept him awake for 89 consecutive hours. Rest and supportive therapy returned him to reasonably good mental and physical health. In his case, prolonged lack of sleep was apparently a break-the-camel's-back burden imposed on pre-existing psycho-pathologic tendencies.

Another man, judged to be slightly psychopathic, informed investigators that sleep is useless, a contemptible habit, that he could get along without it and proposed to prove it. He was given a watchman's clock to punch every 10 minutes. During 231 consecutive hours, nearly 10 days and nights, he failed only a few times to punch the clock on time. The failures could account for only about 5 hours of sleep stolen from the 231 hours, although he could have had some sleep snatches of less than 10 minutes. Beginning on the fourth day, he had hallucinations, became confused and irrational, accused investigators of spoiling the experiment, and finally became so unmanageable that the experiment was ended. Most insomniacs would feel that the man was crazy to begin with.

However, mildly psychotic or paranoid feelings apparently can be aroused in the most healthy and vigorous persons if they are kept awake long enough. What is believed to be the longest sustained period of wakefulness on record—264 hours, or 11 days and nights—was achieved by 17-year-old Randy Gardner of San Diego, Cal. Young Gardner undertook his fortnight of wakefulness as a project for the annual science fair of his school, with the assistance of two classmates. His last three nights of sleeplessness were under the professional observation of W. C. Dement. The youth did not develop any acute psychiatric problems, but he displayed paranoid feelings, irritability, and had one visual hallucination. Shortly after he resumed his usual sleep pattern he was perfectly normal again in all respects.

Sleep deprivation per se does not cause insanity. Nor does it have any permanently deleterious effect on physical functions. No important biochemical changes have been found to result from loss of sleep. Whatever the nature of the need for sleep, it apparently is not essential for keeping the body's chemical activities normal. In general, there are no striking deviations from normal heart action, body temperature, blood pressure, basal metabolism, or composition of blood and urine when sleep is long denied.

Kleitman concludes that "it is clear that a person can remain practically awake for as long as 10 days without any detrimental effect on his physical health." But he can become insufferably cantankerous.

Effects of Sleep Deprivation

The consensus of investigators regarding the behavior of sleep-deprived persons is most interesting.

Their behavior very much resembles that of drunkenness, the effects of a large dose of alcohol. They speak in a slurred, rambling way, and as wakefulness intoxicates them, they fail to recognize or correct mispronunciations. They may walk into walls or bushes with their eyes open and stumble on non-existing steps. Their speech is listless, lacks normal inflection, and is inappropriate to the situation.

Irascibility reminiscent of the "fighting drunk" almost invariably accompanies loss of sleep to some degree. The most mild-mannered persons become ill-tempered under continued efforts to keep them awake (who loves an alarm clock?). This resembles the wildness and unmanageability of children kept up too long after their normal bedtime. One husband-and-wife team who undertook a brief sleep deprivation study refused all social engagements, in order to preserve their public image of amiability. Loss of sleep makes for irritability, an aspect of insomnia that the patient rarely complains of though his associates may. An edgy sleep-hungry person is in no mood to suffer fools gladly, and he can be quite bristly in his human relations. Relief of insomnia benefits others than the patient.

Sleep deprivation studies indicate, and personal experience often corroborates, that it is not very difficult to stay awake for 24 hours. Most of the persons tested do not feel overwhelmingly tired the first night, but feel a little sleepy in the small hours of the morning. They go about their affairs the next day quite efficiently and without outward signs of having gone through a night of experimental insomnia. The second sleepless night is much rougher. The eyes become dry, and subjects are not allowed to read because when quiet they fall quickly into sleep. Attacks of sleepiness are most overwhelming during 2 or 3 hours in early morning, but then diminish, and the subject can do ordinary laboratory work the second day—as long as he doesn't sit down. If he is asked to sit and count his pulse, he usually starts dozing off when he reaches a count of 15 or 20.

To generalize, somewhere around the sixtieth hour, more or less, the sleep-deprived person reaches a plateau of sleepiness. He is about as sleepy as he will get although he may be kept awake another 24 or 48 hours. Evidently the stress of staying awake plus the amount of physical activity necessary to prevent sleep results in a higher chronic level of arousal. The only way to keep a person awake without drugs for many hours is to see to it that he moves his muscles, even if only in talking. If he is permitted to relax and close his eyes, he falls promptly asleep. Muscular weakness is pronounced in persons kept awake for days.

What is the best "natural" way to keep awake, if it is desired to do so for good reason, as in cramming for an examination? *Movement* is by far the most important means of fighting off drowsiness, according to sleep deprivation studies. Get up from your chair, pace the room, stretch. The sleepy motorist who stops for the proverbial cup of black coffee gets a lift from caffeine, but walking to and from the restaurant brushes away some mental cobwebs too. If driving must continue, even talking to yourself moves some muscles and helps to fend off sleep.

It is commonly believed that a sleepless night impairs efficiency the next day, so that less work is done and foolish mistakes are

25

made. But a number of studies, such as those of Wilkinson at Cambridge, indicate that there is little impairment of performance after 3 days of sleeplessness—*provided* that the test situation is a complex and challenging one. Ability-tasks given sleep deprived persons may be monotonous and repetitive, promoting drowsiness, or quite stimulating, promoting alertness. Wilkinson found that "the effect of from 30 to 50 hours of sleep deprivation can vary from almost complete inability to perform a task, to no impairment at all if the situation is a challenging one," as in playing darts or table tennis.

Competition, incentive, motivation, appear to sustain performance at a high level in persons who have gone without sleep for days. Monotonous tasks about which one couldn't care less are performed less efficiently after prolonged loss of sleep. But even these may be performed with normal ability if incentive is added. In one type of test, when subjects are given no information about their performance, lack of sleep causes the usual impairment, but when they are told how well or badly they are doing, impairment is slight. For a period, at least, a stimulating situation apparently can override the effects of sleep loss and sustain performance at a fairly high level.

Tests of groups of sleep-deprived persons show that individuals vary in the degree to which their abilities are impaired by loss of sleep, but in any group there are always some whose performance is not impaired. A useful yardstick of capacity to perform well despite lack of sleep is associated with a higher than normal level of muscle tension. The extent to which a person's muscle tension rises when working, compared with resting, may give a ratio for identifying people whose abilities will be little or much impaired by loss of sleep.

Brain wave records of sleep deprived persons show nothing abnormal, except that EEGs taken for an hour or so during the day indicate greater amounts of light sleep. The EEG shows normal alertness when novel stimuli are given. Sleep-deprived persons given many pages of numbers to be added often add just as correctly as when they are rested, but make fewer additions. A possible explanation of such errors of omission is that subjects fail to respond because they have brief intervals of light sleep. One of the most striking findings of electrophysiologists is that brief, recurrent episodes of light sleep can occur when the subject's eyes are open and he is ostensibly awake. The subject usually heatedly denies that he slept for a second or two but EEG tracings confirm it. It is as if sleep too long denied imposes momentary episodes of "microsleep" upon a tired body.

Can Lost Sleep be Made Up?

If a man who customarily sleeps 8 hours out of the 24 goes for 48 hours without sleep, he should, by simple arithmetic, need to sleep 16 hours to make up for lost rest. Or heroic volunteers who go, say, 5 days and nights without sleep, should need to sleep nearly 2 days to "catch up."

This is not the case. Repayment of the sleep debt is not on an eye-for-an-eye or measure for measure basis. Persons who have been deprived of sleep for many days rarely sleep around the clock when the ordeal is over. This is one of the most striking aspects of sleep deprivation studies.

Colleagues of Oswald at Oxford went on a 48-hour instead of a 24-hour schedule. After each 48-hour period they took as much sleep as they wished. They had regularly taken 7½ to 8 hours of sleep per 24 hours. On the 48-hour schedule they did not take 15 to 16 hours of sleep, but regularly 11 to 12 hours.

More remarkable is the recovery of persons who have gone a long time without sleep. Generously allowed to sleep as long as they please after days of sleep deprival, most subjects sleep 11 to 13 hours and awaken spontaneously. After several nights without sleep, subjects seem to be restored to normal by 14 hours of sleep at the most.

Whatever the nature of the sleep debt, it appears to be paid off immediately in depreciated currency—remarkably fewer hours than the hours of lost sleep. There is some evidence that "recovery" sleep is deeper than usual. It also appears to be of high quality.

The relative ease with which lost sleep is made up is consoling to anyone who, after losing a night's sleep, fears that it will take several days to rebound to normal efficiency. One "lost night" appears to have little effect on performance of tasks one is motivated to do, and normal sleep the following night generally erases the sleep debt. Unfortunately, many insomniacs cannot be sure that they will get a good night's sleep following a bad night—indeed, they often anticipate the contrary—and the assistance of hypnotic agents can be very helpful in restoring normal sleep patterns and avoiding a chronic sleep debt that otherwise has little chance of being fully worked off.

How Much Sleep is Enough?

For every person who spends 4 to 5 hours a night in bed—and there are some—there are thousands who believe that 8 hours, give or take a little, is the "normal" duration of a good night's sleep. This amounts to one-third of 24 hours and seems to reflect some natural law that every hour of wakefulness must be paid for with a half hour of sleep.

But is an 8-hour sleep schedule a law of nature enforced by deep physiological need, or a habit, or an evolutionary pattern rooted in alternations of light and darkness? Some people appear to require relatively little sleep, but it is difficult to measure the amount of sleep they actually get. As has been mentioned, persons deprived of sleep for several days return to normal after sleeping about 12 hours. Thus, a man who stays awake 72 hours "pays" for it, not with a half hour of sleep for each hour of wakefulness, but with one-sixth hour or 10 minutes—a bargain.

In polar regions, darkness or light is continuous for weeks and sleep patterns are not subject to diurnal cycles of day and night or social patterns that compel one to awaken early to get the young-sters off to school. H. E. Lewis studied the sleep habits of members of 5 polar expeditions. The men were at liberty to sleep as long as they liked, irrespective of clock-hours. On the average, members of all 5 expeditions slept just about 8 hours out of the 24. There were no great differences in duration of sleep when men were very active in outdoor activity and when they were confined to huts. Evidently we need as much sleep when we are sedentary as when we do hard physical labor. The findings can be interpreted to mean that 8 hours of sleep is a natural demand based on physiological need, but the nature of the need is not much illuminated.

There are numerous studies of the duration of sleep which include such interesting observations as the comment that women sleep longer than men except in one institution for the insane. Sleep cannot be equated with elapsed time between going to bed and getting up. There is a period of drowsiness before and after sleep, and the average person needs about 20 minutes to fall asleep. Such factors were allowed for in Kleitman's study of 25 subjects who were observed for several thousand nights. Their sleep time averaged 7.5 hours, but there was a range in individuals of 6 to 9 hours. Some subjects awakened spontaneously at about the same time the clock was set for, but many did not. It was concluded that an alarm clock cuts about 35 minutes from the duration of sleep, compared to the time of spontaneous awakening.

Can we get too much sleep? Something in the nature of "luxury sleep," comparable to overeating, has been postulated. It is not uncommon for some persons to awaken with a headache which they attribute, rightly or wrongly, to sleeping too long. One medical investigator reported considerable success with a "sleep diet" which limited the sleep of migraine patients to 7.5 hours. If, allowing for individual variation, there is such a thing as overindulgence in sleep, it presumably continues after mysterious physiologic needs have been satisfied. Psychologic factors are complex and hard to measure. If there is nothing very exciting or necessitous to wake up to, why wake up? Motivation triggers wakefulness. It is impossible to imagine that the most indolent man would oversleep on the morning he is scheduled to catch a plane to Tahiti.

What of those persons who ostensibly do very well with 4 or 5 hours of sleep a night? The first envious thought is that they steal naps they don't admit to or have "microsleeps" they are not aware of. Much of the lore about men who need little sleep concerns legendary figures such as Napoleon and Edison. Napoleon worked at all hours and interspersed brief snatches of sleep, but not even he could abolish a basic need. Before Waterloo, he slept astride a chair while reviewing cheering troops. He could sleep while riding a horse. On the field of Waterloo he sat for hours, much of the time asleep, his head on his arms, and when he had to leave the field he was so drowsy that it was difficult to get him to his horse. A friend of Edison has commented that the inventor "could go to sleep while he was talking to you."

There seems to be no absolute need that sleep be taken in one uninterrupted 8-hour stretch. Less than an average amount of sleep may be sufficient if a nap is added. During the blitz of England in World War II, men and women got much less than their average amount of sleep but remained effective for months provided they got a nap. A common belief that an afternoon nap of adults spoils the next night's sleep was not substantiated in Lewis's studies of polar expedition members. The men had many interruptions of sleep and took many naps. There was no relation between naps and interrupted sleep. The one did not breed the other. Despite plenty of sleep, the men were still able to sandwich in an extra nap.

The catnap of the letdown period at the end of the workday, before or after the evening meal, may occur, Kleitman speculates, at the lowest period of the 90-minute rest-activity cycle, and tide it over. Here is ammunition of a sort for the husband whose wife objects violently to his catching a little snooze on the sofa while she is getting dinner. Naps also afford a means of distributing wakefulness more to one's personal liking, which may not be the distribution favored by social custom or Poor Richard's Almanac. Winston Churchill followed the principle of late to bed and late to rise and did much work at night, but he invariably took a nap of an hour or so after lunch.

Physicians who hear many complaints of insomnia often suspect that the patient gets more sleep than he realizes. Brain wave tracings show that brief episodes of light sleep or near sleep not only can occur while the eyes are open but even while going through the motions of some simple task. If the subject is told that he slept briefly, he usually becomes very indignant and insists that he was meditating, thinking, or brooding creatively. There is drowsiness but some contact with reality when attention wanders on the borderland of sleep. An aptitude for snatching brief periods of unconceded rest may be pronounced in those who are proud of needing only 5 hours of sleep a night.

Sleep Needs at Different Ages

Cats kept in darkness sleep about 20 hours out of the 24. Young infants are popularly believed to sleep as much or more. Some pamphlets for parents assert that small babies are awake only 2 hours in 24. The facts are somewhat different.

One study of 75 newborn babies showed that they slept 16.6 hours a day, on the average, during the first three days of life. Another study of infants under 6 months of age, conducted for 24 weeks under home conditions, showed an average sleep time of 12 to 16 hours a day. By age 3 the child has begun to consolidate his sleep time, for the convenience of parents and the admiration of society, and generally sleeps about 10 hours at night, with naps decreasing.

"Sleep problems" of children, or more often the child's parents, tend to be aggravated around the fifth year, about the time when naps are given up. The transition from two shorter periods of wakefulness to one longer one may be upsetting. When should a child's afternoon nap be given up? There is no arbitrary rule. Most authorities agree that the nap should be abandoned if it delays the onset of sleep in the evening and keeps the child awake after going to bed.

Adolescents have particular difficulty in waking spontaneously. Some attribute this to a transition from juvenile to adult sleep patterns, and others (no doubt including the adolescents) to a heavy burden of homework that leaves a fatigue hangover.

Does adult need for sleep become less with increasing age? Belief that people sleep less as they grow older because they need less sleep is widespread. Not a few elderly people get less than 8 hours' sleep and feel that they do not need so much sleep as when they were younger. Serious question that the need for sleep automatically decreases with age has been raised by Tiller's studies of 83 mentally alert and physically active office patients, not represented to be typical of all older people.

Some of the patients slept much more than 8 hours and believed that their need for sleep increased with advancing age. Others said that their sleep had decreased and they did not like it. They complained bitterly of insomnia and experienced a great deal of discomfort. "Some older patients who not only slept more than 8 hours a night but also took a daily 'siesta' were remarkably free of symptoms." Of the group, 53 were less than 70 years old and 30 were 70 or older.

In all, 33 patients slept fewer than 7 hours and in 18 of these insomnia was a major complaint. Twenty patients who got less than 7 hours of sleep were put on a regimen of increased rest, including a siesta period of an hour or two during the day. After 1 month, three-fourths of the group increased their sleep to 8 hours or more. Their symptoms of continuous fatigue and tension disappeared and they were less apprehensive. All 20 reported a decrease in continuous symptoms, a benefit which appeared to be positively correlated with the increase in sleep.

Undoubtedly the sleep of some older people is curtailed or interrupted by discomforts of organic disease, and primary treatment must be directed toward the underlying condition. Patients whose symptoms were readily explained by organic disease were excluded from Tiller's study. Not all of the improved well-being of the 20 patients was attributed to increased sleep alone. Other factors, such as interruption of compulsive activity, may well have had therapeutic value. But "increased sleep was of considerable importance in producing the symptomatic relief, since persisting symptomatic relief consistently occurred only when the daily sleep was 8 hours or more."

Dogmatic conclusions cannot be drawn from one limited study. However, it seems likely that the optimal sleep requirement of individuals does not change significantly from young adulthood through old age. Belief that old persons do not need so much sleep as younger adults appears to be an example of popular mythology.

The Individuality of Sleep

Researchers can predict with great accuracy that a given group of persons will sleep, say, an average of 7.9 hours per night. But an individual person may sleep 6 or 9 hours. As with other aspects of human behavior, sleep is a matter of considerable personal variability. This, along with the fact that many aspects of sleep are insufficiently explored, makes it very difficult to give arbitrary answers to questions about sleep asked by patients who are concerned about themselves and not the community at large.

Some people sleep so easily that they simply cannot understand, and often cannot sympathize with, the insomniac who is genuinely tortured by sleep inadequacy. The "sleep problem" of some people is not one of sleeping, but of sluggish awakening and inability to get up a good head of steam until several hours have passed. No doubt high "quality" sleep is more restful than low quality sleep, but there are no specific hallmarks of quality, other than that the first couple hours of the night's sleep are usually deepest, and may be more restorative.

It is a commonplace observation that some men and women are "night owls" and others are "early birds." To generalize, early-bird folk are at their best in the morning, work at good fever through the day, but run down early in the evening and go early to bed. Night-owl people don't get fully wound up until late in the morning or early afternoon, are often at their best late at night, and don't get to bed until the wee small hours. Usually the sleep pattern is cut to fit circumstances tolerably well, and only the extremists are conspicuous among multitudes of middle-of-the-roaders. We may recognize tendencies one way or the other in ourselves, in friends, in members of the family.

Neither the night owl or early bird type is "better," nor does either type necessarily get too little or too much sleep. There is simply a different distribution of sleep through the 24 hours. Early bird types are most common, because of the need, reinforced by habit, to be at work, or at least among those present, fairly early in the morning. Night owls tend to gravitate to vocations in which their late in the day alertness is an advantage. There is a considerable element of non-conformity in extreme night owls.

Difficulties can arise if extreme early birds and night owls attempt to mesh their sleep hours. A night owl wife who continually urges her weary early bird husband to go out for an evening on the town risks domestic infelicity, and the early bird husband who nudges a night owl wife out of bed at 5:30 a. m. to fry bacon has stresses in his matrimonial future. If the couple happens to have the same sleep pattern, they can look with righteous scorn upon absurd crack-of-dawn risers or roisterers who never get to bed at a decent hour.

Which comes first, the temperament or the sleep pattern? Or

33

does the pattern depend upon innate physiological rhythms? (see page 40). W. H. Sheldon has associated many aspects of human behavior, including sleep, with varieties of physique. His well-known system of constitutional classification is based on layers of the germ cell from which different organ systems are elaborated in the embryo. Thus, in an endomorph the digestive system is dominant; in a mesomorph, muscle, bone and connective tissue predominate; in an ectomorph, the skin, brain and central nervous system are large relative to body mass. Everyone has all three components, but there are many gradations in the relative predominance of one system to another.

Sheldon's terminology relates physique to temperament in the terms viscerotonic, somatotonic, and cerebrotonic, linked respectively with predominant endomorphy, mesomorphy, and ectomorphy. His shrewd comments about sleep are based on close observation of many thousands of men and women, and supplement the work of electrophysiologists who, as a general thing, tend to regard a sleeper as a sleeper, without much allowance for human variability.

For viscerotonics, Sheldon finds, "Sleep is deep, easy and undisturbed. There is complete relaxation in sleep, the individual becoming limp, like a young child. Going to sleep is easy and happens quickly. There is a great love of sleep and the individual frequently becomes a sleep glutton. It is difficult to wake such a person during the night.

"Somatotonics feel good in the morning. They love to make a lot of noise and greet the sun. Normally they become sleepy or tired rather suddenly at about their usual bedtime, and typically drop off to deep sleep at once upon retiring. Somatotonics thrash about vigorously in sleep. They seem to dream with their muscles."

The cerebrotonic person (whose predominant central nervous system and skin receptors "overexpose" him to the outside world) is a prime candidate for insomnia and is likely to have poor sleep habits. "Insomnia of greater or less degree is almost constant in adult life. Even in childhood, habits of going to sleep are irregular and erratic. If a hypnotic drug is used, heavy dosage is required."

Cerebrotonics are light sleepers. They wake easily and tend to lie

34

in bed in a half awake, half dreaming state. For such persons "the process of getting up in the morning is often an exceedingly painful business. It is only after several hours in bed that this individual descends to really refreshing and recuperative sleep. His deepest sleep is his latest sleep. It may be that for cerebrotonics we should revise the old proverb to read, an hour of sleep in the morning is worth two before midnight. Cerebrotonics often become most alert and do their best work in the evening of the day. They are usually most wide awake around bedtime, and they are often worthless in the early part of the morning."

This sounds very much like a description of a night owl. There are some disparities between Sheldon's opinions and those of electrophysiologists. For instance, EEGs almost always show that the first couple of hours of sleep are deepest, and there is an hypothesis that the quality of sleep gets poorer and poorer as the night wears on and that morning sleep is least refreshing of all. Might there be some unconscious selection of study subjects? Perhaps most of the volunteers for sleep deprivation studies are extraverted somatotonics and viscerotonics. There may be an unrecognized absence of cerebrotonics, introverted, given to insomnia, for whom a cranium bristling with hardware amid watchers bent upon crass observation and interference with sleep would be too horrible to contemplate.

Studies of dreaming (see Chapter 4) might also be deficient in cerebrotonic subjects. According to Sheldon, "Cerebrotonics nearly always, and viscerotonics usually, are more or less aware of the trend of their own dreaming, and can without practice recite their current dreams in some detail. But for individuals of predominant somatotonia an introduction to their own dream world often amounts to revelation."

It may be that there are few somatotonics among the clients of psychoanalysts.

Night Work and Time Zones

Individual sleep patterns seem to persist quite stubbornly along personally established lines. We become geared to sleep and wakefulness on a 24-hour basis. Habit is powerfully reinforced by repetition. But sleep habits are not "all in the mind." They are inter-

35

twined with subtle physiologic rhythms which are also geared to a 24-hour cycle (see page 47). Theoretically, we could adapt with complete success to a diurnal rhythm of 28 or 30 or 32 hours, but there is neither need nor opportunity to do so in the world we live in.

Many people, however, do attempt to shift from their established sleep cycle to a different one when their jobs or circumstances demand it. The most common instance is transfer from day work to night work. Many industries work two shifts, some run around the clock, and many activities—of police, hospitals, public utilities, hotels, transport, turnpike restaurants— require that some employes work at night.

Every night worker at one time had a "normal" 24-hour rhythm of work by day, sleep at night. It might seem that adjustment to night work is a simple matter of rapidly reversing the rhythm. Work the first night. Get so tired that you sleep a long time the next day and are fresh and alert for the following night's work. It isn't quite that way.

Established sleep rhythms cannot be turned on and off overnight. The old rhythm is stubborn and leaves its imprint for a considerable length of time. This is not merely a matter of being unable to sleep well during the day, although night workers often get less sleep than day workers and some studies find that they complain more of fatigue and a variety of ailments, especially digestive ones. Despite good daytime sleep, efficiency at night is often less than full efficiency for some time after an abrupt change in the routine of life.

Sensitive tests indicate a failure of immediate adjustment to a change in routine from day to night. Wittersheim and his associates used performance of a skilled task as a sensitive indicator. Subjects got ample sleep by day and stayed awake for four consecutive nights. Their efficiency at night was considerable impaired, especially in the small hours of the morning. There were many long reaction times, indicating that their vigilance fell briefly to a level of light sleep.

It can take several weeks to make full adjustment to unaccustomed night work or a new rhythm of life activity. Individuals vary in the time they need to make a complete adjustment. Yet 4 or 5 nights seem much too few to overcome the inertia of a pre-existing rhythm.

Employers sometimes rotate night shifts every week or two, either to be kind to the help or because employes demand it. It is not uncommon for hospital nurses to work the night shift for a week and return to day work until their turn rolls around again. This is not the way to do it, if efficiency is an object and the evidence of several studies is to be trusted. Probably it is not even best for the comfort of the worker, who remains under the influence of his old rhythm until the new one gradually takes over after the passage of considerable time. Experts on the matter advise that shifts be rotated as infrequently as possible.

Very sudden changes of sleep rhythms occur more and more frequently with the connivance of jet planes and time zones. One's personal 24-hour rhythm is a matter of "real" elapsed time. The clocks in some country arrived at by overnight flight may say that it is 5 or 6 hours earlier or later than the traveler's body thinks it is. With the advent of supersonic planes it will become commonplace for a person to be 8 hours or even a full half day "off" the time of the zone he lands in. Adjustment to the new time will take at least as long as adjustment of a day worker to a night shift—several days to recover full efficiency. If dealings that require a man to have his wits about him are involved, the traveler may well be disadvantaged. It is something to think about, and perhaps the wily businessman will invite those he deals with to fly over and match wits when the man on his home grounds is in magnificent harmony with his sleep cycle.

The Absent Lesion

From the foregoing it is reasonably clear that sleep is a need, that the need can be suppressed briefly with no great effort and for several days with much effort, that prolonged sleeplessness does not inflict detectable organic injury, and that the need for sleep has the variability of other human functions.

Observations tell something about how the need for sleep expresses itself, but virtually nothing about why the need for sleep exists at all. If sleep is a way of resting the body, why can't we rest

37

just as well without losing consciousness? The need for sleep remains enigmatic. Many theories are teleological: the need for sleep exists, therefore it must serve some purpose beneficial to the organism. Such reasoning may or may not be valid. Vomiting is beneficial if it removes poisons from the stomach but not if it is caused by a brain tumor.

Much sleep research employs the electroencephalograph, an instrument which probes mysteries of the brain and has a considerable aura of awe and magic. Biochemical studies of sleep phenomena have been relatively neglected. It is known that energy extracted from oxidized carbohydrates is converted into high energy ATP molecules, which are rather like molecular storage batteries in our cells. To add another speculation, biochemists may find that sleep is a periodic need to recharge specific cell batteries.

Sleeplessness leaves no lesion, no structural change of which a pathologist can say unequivocally, "this was caused by sleep or lack of it." However, there are many slight physiologic changes that occur with sleep, perhaps coincidentally, and give interesting directions to research.

Chapter 3

THE PHYSIOLOGY OF SLEEP

He may be attending a somnolent symposium or riding home on a commuter's train. His head sinks forward of its own weight. His eyelids droop. His chin drops onto his chest, and with a sudden jerk he lifts his head, blinks, and looks around sheepishly to see if anyone has caught him falling asleep.

This situation will be recognized by not a few people who have fallen into it on occasion and by not a few others who are mildly envious. A combination of muscular relaxation, comfort, droning lecturer, soothing rhythms, and low cerebral vigilance which might be called boredom or inattentiveness, is conducive to sleep. If such elements could be put into an oral tablet, the finest sleeping pill of all time would be available and pharmacology researchers could give up all hope of finding a better one. Improvement of environmental and psychic factors is indeed paramount in alleviation of insomnia, but often it is failure in just these departments which provokes or perpetuates insomnia and the assistance of an hypnotic agent is desirable.

Casual observation reveals many of the superficial aspects of sleep. It also leads to many firmly held but conflicting popular opinions, such as that a snack before bedtime promotes sleep or that it overloads the stomach and disturbs sleep. Is one sleeping posture more restful than another, and does restless threshing about in sleep "waste" a good deal of sleep time? Superficial observation is not wholly to be trusted. An anesthetized or comatose person resembles a sleeping person. There is a vital difference. A sleeper can be aroused easily and quickly.

Many aspects of sleep have been measured and described in physiologic terms. The "meaning" of various phenomena is by no means crystal clear and there is controversy as to significance and cause and affect relations. Many phenomena appear to be related to diurnal rhythms, others to recumbency, and others to interplay of physiologic mechanisms that are not well understood.

Concomitants of Sleep

Relaxation of voluntary muscles is a conspicuous aspect of sleep. The opposite condition of high muscle tension is indeed a good way of postponing sleep. Muscles begin to relax before sleep sets in. Certain muscle groups—of the eyelids, jaw, and neck—are particularly good heralds of drowsiness. The sagging head and drooping eyelids of oncoming sleep engage attention because we tend to judge wide-awakeness by facial expression. But decrease in muscle tonus with sleepiness is widely distributed.

The experience of dozing off while reading in a comfortable chair is not uncommon. Often, the falling of a book from relaxed hands wakes the sleeper with a start. This indicator has been used by investigators to mark the time when sleep begins. The subject is given a light roll of paper to hold in one hand. When it drops from his fingers he is well on the way toward sleep. Some infants sleep on their backs with arms above the head and hands clenched. This has been attributed, cavalierly and inconclusively, to the arboreal habits of ancestors.

Some experimenters have reported that the muscle tonus of sleepers lying in bed is almost non-existent, and that measurements should be made in a sitting-up position for meaningful comparisons. Statements that certain muscle groups do not relax at all in sleep, but actually increase their tonus, are made in many papers about sleep, but without much supporting evidence. The most common statement is that sphincters of the bladder and rectum contract more forcefully during sleep. This could explain continence of urine and feces quite plausibly, but it may be more of a rationalization than a physiologic fact. Oswald denies that retention of urine and feces depends on tightly contracted external sphincters. The internal sphincter, which is not a voluntary muscle, appears to him quite sufficient to serve the end in question. The problem is not entirely academic since it may be involved in complaints of enuresis.

Posture and body movements. Is there a "best position" for restful sleep? Various ideal postures have been highly recommended by various commentators. Even the position of the bed is considered to be highly important by some. Among these was Charles Dickens, who insisted that his bed be aligned in a true north-south meridian with the head at the north. The fetal position is especially decried by the psychoanalytically oriented, who detect in it a craven nocturnal return to the womb. No one has explained very satisfactorily how it would be possible to sleep comfortably in an opposite condition of curvature, or opisthotonos.

The prone or belly-down position is said to be easiest to maintain. Babies often sleep that way, tucking their short legs under them. Legs of adults are longer in proportion to torso length and occasion some vexations of nocturnal arrangement. Proponents of side-sleeping—some say the right side is "right," others say the left—feel that stresses are distributed most equably by drawing up one knee, leaving the other straight or slightly bent. Most often the hip and shoulder joints are major supports and strains are unconsciously eased by using legs and arms as props. A person who sleeps on his back rarely lies absolutely flat. He generally uses one leg to prevent turning over and to throw more weight on the opposite side.

Some conditions of ill health require modifications of sleeping posture. Physicians know that propping up an orthopneic patient relieves his inability to breathe except in an upright position. But a reasonable conclusion to be drawn from many discussions of the matter is that any position is good for a normal healthy sleeper as long as it satisfies him. It won't satisfy him very long. Many studies show that we change posture on the order of a dozen times a night, and some sleepers—perhaps Sheldon's somatotonics who "dream with their muscles"—shift two or three dozen times.

Body movements usually are most numerous during the latter half of the night when sleep is lighter. Our sensory threshold rises in sleep; the intensity of stimuli necessary to make an impression is greater than when we are conscious. Probably the discomfort of lying too long in one position is "felt" during an interval of light sleep, and we make corrective movements. Also, body movements tend to cluster in cycles about an hour and a half apart, corresponding to 90-minute (more or less) "peaks" of light sleep in the rest-activity cycle. There is some evidence that major body movements precede dreaming periods.

We do more tossing and turning through the night than we remember. It has occurred to some people who wake up tired that all this body movement might impair the quality of sleep. It could as well result from sleep of poor quality. But observations of sleepers indicate that very little time is "wasted" in shifting from one posture to another. Body movements are relatively frequent but do not last long. Measurements of elapsed time show that all the night's body movements, if added together, amount to only about 5 minutes of mild exercise. If this is wasted sleep, it's hardly enough to worry about.

Nocturnal jerks. Watch a sleeping dog or cat long enough and you will probably notice a sudden incoordinate jerk of whole or part of the body. Similar "nocturnal jerks" occur in human beings. Few patients bother their doctors about these twitchings which they properly consider to be insignificant, and the prevalence of jerks can only be elicited by questioning. Most patients say they get occasional jerks, some deny them, and a few are apprehensive about them and even blame their spasms on heavy smoking, thus extending the culpabilities of tobacco into an exotic area.

Oswald is of the opinion that everyone has these nocturnal jerks but remembrance is lost in the amnesia of sleep. He questioned 150 people and was convinced that personal estimates are completely unreliable. Separate questioning of husbands and wives revealed that the spouse was the traumatized beneficiary of numerous jerks which the mate did not recall. Probably these peculiar jerks occur only in light sleep, and originate in the cerebral cortex. Muscle tension rises with cerebral vigilance. Apparently the cortex is exasperated into some mysterious focal discharge expressed as a jerk. No harm is done. Persons of nervous temperament seem to have more jerks or to remember them better.

Secretions. We do not have to keep swallowing during sleep. Secretions of nose, mouth, and throat diminish. The salivary glands, in a sense, sleep when we do. In general, the volume of urine secretion is less during sleep—an obvious aid to undisturbed slumber—but the kidneys continue their functions. It is imprudent to rely unduly on subjugation of the kidneys by sleep. Restriction of fluid intake before going to bed is one of the keystones of treatment of enuretic children. Fluids will out; volume of intake is related to volume of output. A distended bladder is one of the physiologic alarm clocks which rouses us to "wakefulness of necessity" to deal with a threat which cannot be temporized with indefinitely.

A great many investigators of renal function in sleep have measured specific gravity, acidity, and electrolyte concentration with much precision. This has not led to a consensus as to the significance of slight differences or the role that sleep per se plays in effecting them. Some of the observed differences seem to result from rest in the horizontal position, with decreased blood flow.

The skin of a sleeper is often slightly moist. One way of measuring sweating is to measure the electrical resistance of the skin, which varies with dryness or moistness. Perspiration appears to increase somewhat during sleep. Indeed, copious amounts may be shed, especially if there is much heat-producing muscular activity. But environmental factors such as room temperature are important and difficult to isolate from the "pure" effects of sleep. Blankets can have an insulating or hot-box effect, retarding evaporation.

Digestion appears to be unaffected or little affected by sleep. Less bile and very little salivary secretion enters the tract. Hunger contractions are just as strong and frequent as in wakefulness, sometimes stronger. Body movement may occur at times of strong stomach contractions. The sigmoid colon is relatively quiescent, but intestinal movement is much the same as in the daytime, appropriate to stages of digestion.

Does the stomach increase or decrease its secretory activities in sleep? There is no general agreement. According to several studies, the volume of gastric juice usually, but not invariably, decreases in sleeping normal subjects. Patients with peptic ulcer may be

43

special cases. In them, stomach acids tend to build up through the night and the patient may be awakened by pain around 2 a. m. Dietary management of peptic ulcer often includes a light snack at bedtime. Sometimes the patient is advised to keep cookies or crackers and milk on a bedside table, for consumption when an alarm clock awakens him before the anticipated onset of early morning pain. The object is to give stomach acids something to work on besides the mucosa of an empty stomach.

The stomach empties at its normal rate regardless of whether its owner is asleep or awake. Some of the disparities of opinion about secretory activities may be related to the presence or absence or changing amount of food in the stomach during the period of observation. Entrance of food into the stomach releases secretin, a hormone which triggers the pancreas gland to release its alkaline digestive juices into the small intestine. Some normal subjects secrete as much acid as peptic ulcer patients but sleep through it indifferently. Perfectly valid findings may differ because of subtle biological differences in subjects.

Digestion is not incompatible with sleep. On the contrary, drowsiness commonly follows a meal if one relaxes in a quiet place. More blood is pooled in the abdomen. Dyspeptics are notoriously sensitive to goings-on in their gastrointestinal tracts, and for them a heavy evening meal or a going-to-bed repast may well disturb sleep. For the normal person who can follow the dictum that the healthy gut thrives best when ignored, there is no reason, as far as sleep investigators can discover, to anticipate that a pre-retiring snack that is not unwholesome or gigantic will have any other effect on sleep than encouragement.

Breathing in sleep is noisier than in wakefulness. Probably this is the basis for the misconception that respiration in sleep is deeper. About the only constant finding is that breathing in sleep is relatively regular and even, slower and shallower in deep sleep. Mere observation of the rise and fall of the chest is not very informative, and refined measurement with instrumental aid is difficult because the necessary hardware impedes the subject's natural movements. However, all observers note a decrease in ventilation of the lungs in sleep. Carbon dioxide tension in arteries and the percentage

44

of carbon dioxide in alveolar air rises with sleep. The noisiness of breathing in sleep may be related to altered muscular tone in the upper respiratory passages. The predominance in sleep of chest-breathing over the abdominal breathing of wakefulness is mentioned in many reports. At times, respiration in sleep is so periodic as to resemble the Cheyne-Stokes type.

Reflex excitability is a complex phenomenon, and there is no general agreement about changes in sleep. Most authorities agree that reflexes which do not disappear are weakened and the reflex time is lengthened. The diminished cough reflex remains sufficiently active to maintain a clear airway. Usually it is stated that tendon reflexes, such as the knee jerk, disappear or diminish. Sleep raises the irritability threshold of the central nervous system and this, together with muscular relaxation, could well explain a reduction in reflex excitability.

The *basal metabolic rate* (BMR) is lowered about 10 per cent in sleep. Basal heat production decreases with muscle relaxation. Some heat loss is associated with peripheral vasodilatation. The BMR during sleep is considered by many to be the "true" basal level. Body temperature, which diminishes with sleep, is one aspect of diurnal rhythms.

Cardiovascular changes. Slowing of the heart rate is a characteristic sign of sleep. The rate is generally reduced about 10 beats per minute but reductions of 30 beats have been recorded. Daytime naps seem to have little effect on the heart rate, which is not a very reliable indicator of depth of sleep. Loud noises, nightmares, alarming stimuli, can raise the sleeper's blood pressure and set his heart to pounding. Blood pressure, especially the systolic, falls in sleep. High blood pressure in the waking state generally falls in sleep to systolic levels of healthy persons. The horizontal position with reduced blood pressure, slowed heart rate, lower metabolic rate, and muscular relaxation, undoubtedly influences cardiovascular changes in sleep, but some factors, such as the rise of sensory threshold, may be attributable to sleep itself.

Blood. Large numbers of studies of composition of the blood in normal sleep have led to what Kleitman designates as "strange notions and theories concerning the physiology of sleep." He cites

45

as an example the theory that calcium partially disappears from the blood and is taken up by the brain during sleep. Most constituents of the blood are decreased during sleep, but nearly all changes in composition are explainable as effects of the horizontal versus the upright posture.

It may be that the blood holds mysterious clues as to the nature of sleep. There appears to be a strange eosinophil cycle. Kleitman remarks that "when you wake up your eosinophils go down." Do we need more of these formed elements of the blood when we sleep than when we are awake? Do our blood-forming tissues work with specialized efficiency while we sleep? Where do our eosinophils go when we wake up? It is an interesting puzzle, of uncertain significance.

There is general agreement that endocrine glands, particularly the pituitary and adrenal, are involved with phenomena of sleep and wakefulness. It is not surprising that the concentration of epinephrine, the "arousal hormone" of the adrenal medulla, is lowered in human plasma during sleep. Dell mentions the role of the posterior pituitary:

"We know well that in the evening and as we go to sleep the water content of the blood increases and there is an augmentation of the secretion of antidiuretic hormone (ADH). Moreover, sleep can be induced by giving water together with an injection of ADH. If this is done in a whole ward of patients at a time of day when they do not normally sleep, you will see that most of them will fall asleep."

Eyes. One of the first signs of sleepiness is drooping eyelids. When the eyes are open, a peculiar dull look that is hard to describe but easy to recognize suggests sleepiness. We fight against sleep by blinking the eyes. Tear-gland secretion diminishes during drowsiness. The eyes feel dry and gritty; the "sandman" arrives. Once the eyes are closed, sleep comes rapidly.

The pupils are constricted in sleep and generally do not constrict further if exposed to light. We do not hold our eyelids tightly closed in sleep. The eyelids of a sleeper can be opened gently. In some experiments, the eyelids of subjects are stuck open but they fall asleep anyway. An ocular sign of sleepiness is double vision, inability to fixate a point with both eyes despite extreme effort to do so.

Belief that the eyes roll upward and outward in sleep appears to be ill-founded. This position is most uncomfortable, at least if one attempts to maintain it voluntarily for more than a few seconds. The eyes in sleep may roll into any position. They do not hold a fixed position throughout the night. Bursts of rapid horizontal and vertical eye movements are believed to be characteristic of dreaming. Rolling movements of the eyes are common during drowsiness.

Rhythms of Sleep and Wakefulness

We go to bed and get up at accustomed hours—most of the time. In our affairs we conform to rhythms of day and night for prudence and profit, convenience and necessity. Much of this is learned behavior, more or less externally imposed. At the same time we learn the rhythms, internal rhythms, of a great many body functions. More precisely, these biologic rhythms impose a sort of enforced and unconscious education upon us. Our sleep habits are an amalgamation of internal and external rhythms which resist alteration quite forcefully once they are firmly established.

Changes during sleep of metabolism, secretion, excretion, and other physiologic functions have previously been described. No doubt a great number of other biologic periodicities tick away in the body like thousands of molecular metronomes. Alternations of rest and activity are imposed by the wisdom of the body, and the alternations seem to be rather more frequent than might be supposed. If in mid-afternoon we are listless and work goes slowly, we might blame it on being caught in a trough of our basic rest-activity cycle.

Studies of infants indicate that alternations of muscular activity and rest occur about an hour apart. In one study, infants on self-demand schedules woke up and demanded at intervals which were multiples of the hourly cycle. This is soon coupled with a feeding or gastric activity cycle of 3 to 4 hours. Gradually a 24-hour cycle, which includes social periodicities, is acquired. The child outgrows his naps and eventually consolidates sleep into about 8 hours, the adult pattern.

Adults are geared to operate on a 24-hour cycle which does not entirely obscure the shorter fluctuations of the basic rest-activity cycle. Everyday experience confirms that our mental and physical capacities do not remain at the same unvarying level throughout 16 hours of wakefulness. We do not start the day with a charge of energy like sand in an hourglass which trickles away steadily until it is exhausted at bedtime. There are surges and letdowns, accomplishments and coffee breaks.

Evidence of a more scientific nature is furnished by EEG records of sleepers. These show that cycles of light and deeper sleep occur in rhythmic succession. Kleitman observed the sleep of 33 subjects for 71 nights and noted a regular succession of cycles of EEG variation through 7 to 8 hours of sleep. The time between one crest of light sleep (nearest to wakefulness) to the next averaged 70 to 90 minutes. This is construed to be a reflection of a basic rest-activity cycle which intrudes itself in sleep to make us relatively more alert or slumbrous.

The same alternations of rest and activity are thought by many to occur during wakefulness as well. Apparently the hourly rest-activity cycle of infancy persists throughout life and throughout the 24 hours. Various studies show differences in length of the cycle in individual adults—70 minutes, 90 minutes, 110 minutes. But a swing from alertness toward dullness, from activity toward rest, seems to occur on a 1 to 1½-hour schedule when we are awake and when we are asleep. In wakefulness, muscular activity, cerebral excitement—a deadline or an argument—and strong motivation can mask a tendency to let down periodically. What physiologic mechanisms may underlie this apparent rest-activity cycle of approximately 90 minutes? Part of it may be explained by the body's activities as a heat machine.

Fatigue, Alertness, and Body Temperature

Cryotherapy—treatment with cold—in its modern forms is relatively new to medicine. A familiar example is hypothermia which may be employed preparatory to open heart surgery. Reduction of body temperature slows metabolic processes and lessens the oxygen needs of tissues. Sufficient reduction of body temperature brings mental torpor and unconsciousness although vegetative processes

48

continue at a low but adequate level under controlled conditions.

The opposite condition of elevated body temperature, within limits, is characteristic of activity and alertness. Most protoplasmic activities, which are chemical in nature, are accelerated by a rise in temperature. Thus it might be that when we warm up, we're wide awake, and when we cool off we tend to sleep. Such fluctuations within the 24-hour sleep and wakefulness cycle have been found to occur quite consistently.

The most intensive investigations of the subject have been made by Kleitman. He discovered "quite by accident" that daily ups and downs in ability to stay awake parallel fluctuations in body temperature. In broad generalization, body temperature is at its peak in the middle of the waking period and at its minimum during sleep. Best performance and lowest fatigability coincide roughly with temperature peaks, sleepiness with temperature troughs.

It has long been known that "normal" body temperature of 98.6° F. is not inflexible but has slight up and down swings during 24 hours. The range of fluctuation, from 1 to 2 degrees, is not great but evidently is sufficient to cause, or reflect, changes in our state of alertness or tiredness. According to 18,000 readings made by Kleitman, maximum temperature occurred on the average at 2 p. m., minimum at 2 a. m. This coincides well with activities of the honest burgher, who is hard at work in early afternoon and sound asleep in early hours of the morning.

There are many individual differences, but maximum and minimum temperatures are usually separated by 12 hours. Kleitman distinguishes 2 types of temperature-efficiency curves. Some people learn better in the morning, others in the evening. Early bird or morning people arrive at their temperature peaks early in the day, shortly before or shortly after noon. The opposite true for evening people.

Body temperature is not under voluntary control. Nevertheless, it can be informative and perhaps comforting to recognize swings in one's own cycle. If drowsiness descends at unwanted times, it is consoling to think that one is not losing pep but is transiently caught in a trough of low temperature. Body temperature effects are evident in wakefulness as well as sleep. The alertness of sleep-deprived

49

persons waxes with a rise in body temperature and wanes with its fall. Performance is worse immediately on getting up in the morning. Body temperature then is lower than it was just before going to bed.

Fortunately, performance immediately after getting up is commonly limited to dressing, shaving, downing toast and coffee, and matters which do not demand extreme virtuosity. Grumpiness at the breakfast table may not be incivility but low temperature. Fluctuations of body temperature appear to arise mainly from variations in muscular activity. As muscle tonus rises, so does temperature. At some point, fatigue induces muscle relaxation and accompanying downturn in temperature, along with some dampening of cortical activity. Periods of mild lassitude and letdown during the day may coincide with reductions in temperature that do not necessarily cause extreme drowsiness. We seem to need to "warm up" in the most literal sense, not unlike athletes preparing for a contest, to reach a peak of mental and physical efficiency. Hopefully, activities such as running for a bus or getting youngsters off to school put us in good vigor for the working day.

The 24-hour temperature rhythm appears not to be inborn, but to appear in the second year of life. Once established, it is remarkably stubborn. Continuous bed rest for several days usually does not abolish it. The cycle can be inverted, at least to a tolerable degree, as by a shift from day to night work, but individuals vary a good deal in the time required to establish a new temperature curve. Perhaps satisfactory inversion is more easily achieved by the young than by the old. One study has shown that traces of the old temperature rhythm persisted in nurses 5 to 6 weeks after they shifted from day to night duty.

"For each individual," Kleitman concludes, "there probably exists a drowsiness temperature level above which it is easy to remain awake and below which it is progressively harder to do so."

Hibernation

Cold triggers hibernation, which superficially resembles sleep. Low body temperature is one feature of hibernation. The cold

50

stimulus, however, is external, and the rhythm is seasonal rather than diurnal.

The most popular misconception is that bears hibernate in winter. Actually, bears go into prolonged winter sleep during which body temperature is maintained within 15° or so of normal.

Bears, like man, are *homoeothermic* organisms which maintain body temperature at more or less constant levels by means of thermoregulation. When outside temperature becomes lower, more fuel is consumed to keep body temperature at its normal level. In extreme prolonged cold, the body begins to lose heat faster than it can produce it, and body temperature falls sufficiently to produce lethargy and death. *Poikilothermic* creatures are not able to adjust body temperature to environment. When external temperature falls, body temperature falls, vital functions slow down and a state of "cold torpor" supervenes.

True hibernators such as woodchucks and ground squirrels have evolved a peculiar way of surviving long stretches of cold weather and starvation. They reduce energy expenditure to a minimum and conserve calories by spending the winter or parts of it in a lethargic state known as hibernation. Under stress of cold, hibernators can switch from their normal homoeothermic state to a poikilothermic state. Initially, cold stimulates the body to produce more heat, just as in non-hibernators, but thermoregulating mechanisms become inefficient and body temperature falls slowly. However, the animal does not die as other mammals do if cold is uninterrupted. As soon as body temperature becomes critically low, heat regulation ceases altogether and the animal becomes poikilothermic.

This changeover is the outstanding specific physiologic feature of hibernation. If the body falls to too low a temperature, a switch back to homoeothermia occurs. Heat production is resumed and may cause sufficient rise in body temperature to wake the hibernator. Vital functions fall to a very low level to conserve energy which is doled out sparingly. The heart rate of hibernating ground squirrels may decrease from 300 to 2 beats per minute and the respiratory rate may slow to 1 to 3 respirations per minute. These functions usually slow in human sleep, but by no means to such extreme degree. In deep hibernation there is little or no spontaneous electrical activity of the brain, and this too is different from the relatively high activity of the brain in human sleep.

Do sleep and hibernation have a common cause of onset? There is no definitive proof, but the proximity of activating centers in the brain suggests an association, possibly coincidental. Paavo Suomalainen of the University of Helsinki has pointed out that brain centers which reduce body temperature and protect against overheating are located in the anterior hypothalamus, and centers which increase body temperature to protect against cold are located in the posterior hypothalamus. In general, these areas correspond respectively to centers of sleep and wakefulness.

Suomalainen's studies indicate that specific neurosecretory cells in the hypothalamus produce a secretion which plays an essential role in hibernation. As yet it has not been demonstrated that there is any connection between this secretion and the rhythm of sleep and wakefulness. It remains to be proved that the brain, in a sense, "secretes" drowsiness and alertness.

Sleep and Wake Centers

The geography of the brain has been well mapped and its continents, islets and strata have been labeled in great detail. Gross aspects of the brain were well known to ancient anatomists who had no means of unraveling mysteries of a pinkish-gray mass of tissue which crudely resembles a cauliflower with a stalk hanging down. The human brain, which weighs about 3 pounds but floats almost weightless in the cranium, is the most complex organ in creation. Functions of some of its areas have been fairly well delineated, particularly with the aid of the electroencephalograph and probing electrodes.

The concept that sleep and wake centers exist somewhere in the brain is very old. Modern technology has not wholly resolved the problem. There are controversies and uncertainties as to the exact role of clusters of brain cells in facilitating sleep and wakefulness. The idea that sleep is a passive phenomenon requiring no mechanism persists, as does the more sophisticated idea that if a center exists, it is for wakefulness. Interactions of the cortex and lower brain centers are speculative. The concept of 2 antagonistic sleep

CORTEX STIMULATED

Sleep   Full Arousal

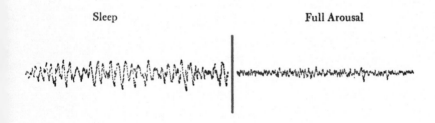

RAS STIMULATED

Sleep   Full Arousal

Interactions between the cerebral cortex and reticular activating system are demonstrated in EEG records of a sleeping animal. Electric current was applied separately to the brain surface and to the brain stem. In each case a typical waking pattern resulted, but response to stimulation of the reticular activating system was more abrupt than response to cortical stimulation.

and wake centers operating independently of the cortex is waning. Nevertheless, in the past decade neurophysiologists have come close to a consensus regarding the anatomical reality of a mechanism having as its main function the maintenance of the waking condition.

H. W. Magoun and Giuseppe Moruzzi, working at Northwestern University in 1949, found that they could awaken a drowsing cat by stimulating a tiny area of the brain stem with a small electric current. The cat's awakening was like arousal from normal sleep. Electric stimulation of local brain cells caused the pattern to change from sleep to wakefulness.

Here was a major landmark in neurophysiology, soon confirmed by other investigators, which led to intensive studies of the brain stem, a structure which previously had been somewhat neglected in favor of the ostentatious cerebral cortex. "Probably never in the history of brain study has there been a mine as rich as the brain stem has been for investigators of the past decade," J. D. French wrote in 1960.

The brain stem or "stalk" is continuous with the spinal cord. It is a core of brain tissue which includes the reticular formation, sub-thalamus, hypothalamus, midline thalamus and septal region. It is now known that these structures contain the principal integrative mechanisms of the brain.

The Reticular Formation

A tiny nerve network in the central part of the brain stem is called the reticular formation. It is no bigger than your little finger, a David to the cerebral Goliath. It is not a uniform entity, but a diffuse grouping of different kinds of cells with numerous, different, and complementary functions. A rousing collection of cells is called the reticular activating system (RAS).

Destruction of the reticular formation brings hopeless coma. It is essential to arousal, wakefulness, consciousness, awareness of the world. With an intact cortex but a damaged reticular formation, an individual is a helpless blob of protoplasm. Among other things, alternations between sleep and wakefulness appear to be imposed by fluctuations of excitement in the reticular formation. All stimuli

54

Postulated sleep and arousal mechanisms of the brain (schematic).

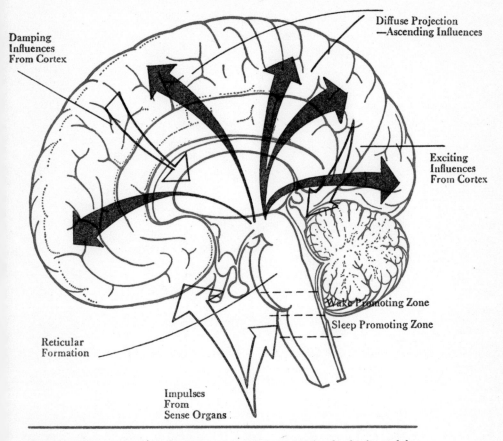

Diffuse Projection
—Ascending Influences

Damping
Influences
From Cortex

Exciting
Influences
From Cortex

Wake Promoting Zone

Sleep Promoting Zone

Reticular
Formation

Impulses
From
Sense Organs

Impulses from a sense organ travel to a sensory area in the brain and by
branching pathways into the reticular formation. A stimulus traveling through
the reticular formation can awaken the entire brain through a diffuse projection system which does not transmit specific messages. The cerebral cortex
judges "meanings" of stimuli. Descending influences from the cortex can
dampen or excite the reticular activating system. Hypothetical wake-promot-
ing and sleep-promoting centers shown in the diagram are based on animal
experiments in which prolonged sleep or wakefulness resulted when areas
were cut through at approximately the levels indicated.

which wake us or keep us awake are thought to do so by activating the mechanisms of the reticular activating system. Anything which interferes with these mechanisms—for example, oxygen deficiency or hypoglycemia—abolishes consciousness.

Branches of all the great sensory nerve trunks of the body stream into the reticular formation. Sensory signals go to the cortex by direct pathways but also feed through the reticular formation. Nerve impulses ascend from the reticular formation to the cortex and descend from it to the spinal cord. The reticular system is in good position to filter hordes of impulses, or as French expresses it: "The reticular system possesses the remarkable capacity to monitor all information which the brain receives, accepting only a limited amount of sensory input at any one time. Were it not thus, utter chaos would reign, since the cerebral structures could not possibly cope with the overwhelming deluge of impulses with which they are bombarded every moment."

An apparent function of the reticular system is to act as a vigilant sentinel, a general alarm system, a pacemaker for the rest of the brain, a mechanism for arousing and keeping the cortex awake. It delivers no specific messages. The reticular activating system responds in the same way to any sensory stimulus: by arousing the brain. The cortex may "decide" that the call to arousal is trivial; it may send descending impulses to pacify the brain stem.

Cortical regions project to the brain stem, and descending cortical impulses can reduce as well as augment the excitability of the reticular system. Conduction of nerve impulses is not one-way, but recurrent over intricate feedback circuits. Ability of the cortex to discriminate among stimuli persists during sleep, as in the familiar example of the mother who wakes to her baby's cry but not to a banging shutter. The cortex decides whether or not a stimulus is worth waking up to, but the stimulus is transmitted by impulses ascending from the reticular activating system. There is a lapse of time before the cortex wakes us to consciousness. Everybody experiences this when the alarm clock goes off. The stirring auditory signal is transmitted instantly by the excited reticular formation to a cortex which is still asleep. It takes a second or two to recognize and respond to the stimulus by shutting off the alarm.

From a physiologic point of view, we apparently not only passively fall asleep but actively go to sleep. Just as wakefulness implies active apprehension of the external world, so may sleep reflect *active disinterest* in the external world. Neurophysiologists speak of active and passive "reticular deactivation." Passive deactivation is a slackening of reticular excitation arising from diminished bombardment by everyday external stimuli. Active deactivation is brought about by interplay of cerebral and reticular formation impulses. Impulses from the cerebral cortex can excite the reticular formation and others can dampen it and promote sleep.

There is no doubt that areas in the reticular formation, which might be called sleep and wakefulness centers, are essential for initiating, modifying and maintaining states of arousal or "consciousness." But the concept of discrete, autonomous sleep-and-wake centers must take cognizance of extensive feedback circuits of great complexity. Dell has suggested that the idea of two antagonistic centers of sleep and wakefulness "is better replaced by the idea of the interplay of numerous cerebral structures, capable of assembling and reflecting, by their level of activity, all the stimuli arising from the continually changing external and internal world."

Physiologic Pathways

It is easier to measure measurable phenomena than to assign these phenomena to unquestioned places in the hierarchy of sleep and wakefulness. It is none the less tempting to speculate on the manner in which observed physiologic elements may effect fluctuations of consciousness. Sleep researchers, who are as human as anybody, engage in informed speculation.

The endocrine system plays a role in rhythms of sleep and wakefulness. Hormones are chemical communicators, relatively slow in comparison with flashing impulses of the nervous system. Many hormones are secreted by cells, including some cells of the nervous system, that have no recognizable glandular arrangement. Interactions of the nervous and endocrine systems have long been known, but awareness of the closeness of this association is relatively recent.

It is known that descending impulses from the brain stem can bring the release of adrenal hormones. An injection of epinephrine promotes arousal. Discoveries of the past decade have assigned a controlling influence over the endocrine system to portions of the brain stem. French states that "this control is expressed through action of the hypothalamus on the anterior pituitary body, and it is now evident that pituitary action on all target organs is subject to central influence. Pituitary-adrenocortical mechanisms are particularly heavily implicated in central nervous system function." The concentration of epinephrine is lowered in human sleep, apparently by brain stem orders to reduce a hormone of excitation.

Low muscle tonus and diminished reflexes are characteristic of sleep. One function of reflex systems is to keep muscles in a state of partial contraction or resting tension—"tone." The reticular activating system exerts some control over reflexes and apparently participates in regulating all motor activities. The drooping eyelids, sagging jaw, and lax neck muscles that herald sleep evidently respond, at least in part, to a reticular activating system that prepares for slumber.

Some differentiation has been made of functions of various levels of the reticular formation. The lower reticular formation has centers for acceleration of heart and breathing rates and the lower brain stem has mechanisms that promote EEG signs of sleep. The upper reticular formation is thought to contain excitatory mechanisms concerned with physiologic drives such as hunger, thirst, and mating. Satisfaction of such drives tends to be followed by sleep. Regulatory measures are exerted at least partly in the hypothalamus, in close proximity to sleep-and-wake centers and thermostatic centers which respond to cold and warmth and regulate body temperature.

Diminution of body temperature, heart and breathing rates, muscle tonus, reflexes, excitation, is characteristic of sleep. Physiologic pathways to such modifications stream from the brain stem. But the discriminating cerebral cortex can dampen a usurpative reticular formation if necessary. We can become habituated to some stimuli, especially auditory ones, so that they no longer arouse us from sleep. Human and animal studies have shown that as few as 5 to 10 repetitions of an auditory stimulus can produce habituation. The stimulus which originally aroused the sleeper no longer does so, although a slight change in the sound, recognized as a different alarm, will do so. The cerebral cortex, though "asleep," must decide that a given stimulus is not worth paying attention to; the reticular formation sends no specific message, only a general clamor for attention. Descending impulses from the cortex inhibit the reticular activating system to avert interruption of sleep by foolish false alarms. Habituation to monotonous stimuli which enter the reticular formation over and over again would be expected to weaken the usual response of arousal, and sleep would tend to appear or continue. Habituation can occur at both cortical and brain stem levels. Such mechanisms are not entirely inconsistent with Pavlov's internal inhibition theory of sleep, which might be called learning not to respond.

No unified theory of sleep has emerged from physiologic studies. Psychologic factors are important and indeed may be conspicuous in aberrations of sleep that come to a physician's attention.

Chapter 4

PERCHANCE TO DREAM

Who has never awakened without a sense of relief that behavior in a dream will forever remain unknown to the world at large? Who has never felt a twinge of regret that some delightful dream episode was interrupted by rude return to reality? Who has never felt the lifting of an immense burden when some harrowing scenario proves to be "just a dream"?

Dreams have entertained, terrified, solaced and mystified mankind since the beginning of time. The dream as portent and prophecy is long out of fashion except among the credulous. Serious studies of dream life have largely been psychologically or psychiatrically oriented, paying no little attention to the presumed symbolism of anything that is elongated or boxlike. Much stress has been laid on the *content* of dreams, little or none on the *processes* that go on in that dark chamber between the dreamer's ears. For this there has been the best of reasons. Tools to pry into the hidden world of dreams have been quite unsatisfactory.

The development of objective techniques within the past decade has begun to give some glimmers of insight into the mechanisms and functions of dreaming. The newer methodology is not infallible. It cannot impale a dream upon an electrode or do a post mortem on a nightmare. But it satisfies the rigors of controlled and repeatable experiment and yields most engaging data.

A current hypothesis is that dreaming is a unique and essential state of being, associated with but quite different from the sleeping state. The familiar statement that we sleep one-third of our lives may need recasting. It is true that a 75-year-old man has slept 25 years. But he has spent 5 of his sleep-years dreaming. This is a sufficient fraction of human life to warrant investigation of the stuff that dreams are made of.

Labors of "dream detectives" are of the most onerous sort. The investigator must maintain sleepless vigilance the whole night through, attending instruments which record the brain waves, eye flutters, body movements, snores and respiration of a sleeper in an adjacent room. Occasionally the researcher may wake the sleeper at onset of dreaming, or sprinkle water on his face, or ring an electric bell, or note the occurrence of external stimuli such as a crash of thunder or the roar of a jet plane. In other studies he may watch hypnotic light patterns on an oscilloscope activated by brain cells of a drowsy cat.

The fascination of unresolved questions sustains tedious research. Is dreaming a creative process? Might one tap a great source of power by feeding the right "mix" into dreams—perhaps by giving a chemical compound prescribed by a physician? Kekule, a nineteenth century chemist, had a dream in which he saw a snake rolling along with its tail in its mouth. In a flash of inspiration, he "saw" the structure of the benzene ring. The opening lines of "Kubla Kahn" occurred to Coleridge in a dream. But the general experience of mankind is that dreams of omnipotence, of stupendous revelation, of prodigious clarity of intellect, tantalizingly elude one's grasp in the cold light of dawn.

Sir Humphry Davy, discoverer of nitrous oxide, had euphoric dreams when under the influence of the gas. His emotions were "enthusiastic and sublime"; he made "great discoveries"; ideas were organized with consummate ease. But when he tried to recall his ideas they were "feeble and indistinct." Finally he was able to recall one of his great ideas and inscribe it in a sentence: "Nothing exists but thoughts!" Thus do sublime visions collapse into nonsense sentences. Perhaps those who experiment with hallucinogenic drugs are tormented by the most cruel of illusions, that of vast accomplishment without effort.

Does everybody dream? Do dreams have an essential function? What is the brain doing when we dream? Is the dream a slight touch of madness that keeps us sane? What happens if we are prevented from dreaming? How many times a night do we lapse (or ascend) into dreaming? Can events of long duration be compressed into a dream lasting only a minute or two? To these and many other questions there are some fairly convincing answers, much newly informed speculation, and data that render many older speculations obsolete.

Benchmarks of the Dream

How can an observer know that a sleeper is dreaming? One objective indicator was discovered by accident in Nathaniel Kleitman's laboratory at the University of Chicago in 1953. Eugene Aserinsky, a graduate student, observed that the eyes of infants, when sleep set in, made slow movements under closed lids, stopped, began again from time to time, and were the first detectable movements when the infant woke up. This interesting ocular behavior was next looked for in adult sleepers, who, in addition to the slow eye movements of infants, exhibited rapid, jerky eye-rollings which tended to occur in clusters lasting anywhere from 3 to 50 minutes. Periods of rapid eye movement appeared and disappeared in cyclic fashion through the night.

Electroencephalograph tracings showed that rapid eye movements coincided strikingly with low-voltage brain waves typical of light sleep (Stage 1), closest to the waking state. At the same time, the sleeper's heart rate and breathing rate usually increased.

All of this suggested some sort of emotional stirring in the sleeper. Might he be dreaming? The obvious procedure, obviously applied, was to wake the sleeper and quiz him. Conjecture was confirmed. Subjects aroused during or shortly after the termination of rapid eye movements almost always said they were dreaming. But they seldom recalled dreaming if aroused when rapid eye movements were absent.

In short, eye-and-brain recordings appeared to afford an objective means of identifying dreaming periods, marking off the landmarks of fantasy. With various refinements of instrumentation, objective indicators of dreaming have proved to be quite reliable, though some sleepers, at some times, "break the rules." Dream-identifying techniques of course tell nothing about the content of dreams. But they enable the presence, frequency, duration, and rhythms of dreams to be measured, and associations with many variables to be spotted. It is also possible for unfeeling researchers to deprive a sleeper of dreams by waking him whenever a dream begins—an act as heinous as taking candy from a baby, were it not for worthy motivations.

EEGs and REMs

In the esoteric terms of sleep scientists, EEGs are electroencephalograms, REMs are rapid eye movements, and EOGs are electro-oculograms or continuous tracings of eye movements. The well-caparisoned subject prepared for dream studies has a cranium plastered with electrodes with flexible leads which run to recording devices in an adjacent room. This armament is lightly borne and does not interfere with sleep.

Commonly, 3 or 4 silver disk electrodes are pasted to the head. Others are taped to the skin above and below or on either side of one eye. These record changes in potential between the cornea and retina that occur when the eyeball moves. Other electrodes may be placed in the chin region to register muscle tonus.

A significant accompaniment of dreaming is great relaxation of muscles. Motor muscles are almost without tonus. One might expect that a twisting, turning sleeper is in the throes of a dream. On the contrary, we usually lie very quiet when we are busy with a dream, and we would seem to an observer to be "sleeping like a baby." However, major body movements during dream periods may sometimes occur. There is some evidence that twisting, turning, and posture changes during apparent dreaming may mark the interval between the end of one dream fragment and the beginning of another—like the restlessness of old-time movie audiences when the projectionist flashed the sign, "Two minutes while we change reels."

Brain wave patterns are generally considered to be better indicators of dreaming than rapid eye movements. Although characteristic

EEGs and REMs usually occur simultaneously, this is not always the case. Dreams can and sometimes do occur in the absence of rapid eye movements.

Why do our eyes move at all when we dream? There are no clear-cut answers. But it is tempting to speculate, as some informed researchers do, that REMs occur because we look at dream events in much the same way that we would look at the same events in real life. We scan a horse race with our eyes, whether it is a dream race or a real one. But if we look at a snapshot of a horse there is little eye movement. Similarly, in "passive" dreams where nothing very lively is happening, an absence of rapid eye movements would be understandable.

Most REMs are horizontal, corresponding to predominant movements of the eyes in the waking state. Upward-rolling or downcast glances account for relatively little visual exertion. Some sleepers who exhibited vertical eye movements, when asked what they had been dreaming about, said that they had been watching a man climbing a ladder, or a balloon dropping leaflets, or similar events in which vertical scanning would have been appropriate in the waking state. However, some rapid eye movements are so furious and intense that it is hard to think of a natural situation that would evoke such ocular gymnastics, unless it be the situation deplored by the girl in the song who complained, "Ma, he's making eyes at me." The possibility remains that the odd eye movements we unconsciously indulge in when sleeping may be triggered by the firing of unknown nervous mechanisms, independent of or in addition to what we are seeing in our dreams.

Dreams are not necessarily or always visual. Congenitally blind persons do not have visual dreams or rapid eye movements. Persons who "have visions," or "hear voices," may be hallucinated, but they may merely be dreaming; the borderlines are shadowy. Dreams in which talking, music, voices, are the only remembered elements are common in persons who have strong auditory interests. Tactile elements also appear in dreams. A few deaf-mute subjects have reported dreams in which they "talk" with their fingers. As Kleitman has remarked, "One dreams as one thinks."

A timetable for a good night's dreaming is as follows:

Fall asleep and slide rapidly down the brain wave incline from Stage 1 (light sleep) through Stages 2 and 3 of increasing sleep-depth to Stage 4 (deep sleep). This first sleep of the night is dreamless, but prepares the way for dreaming. It lasts about an hour. Next, climb back to Stage 1 in which the brain functions as actively as in the most alert waking state. Researchers call this the "emergent" phase in which ascent from deep sleep triggers the first dream period of the night. It last about 10 minutes.

Thereafter, dream periods follow in cycles spaced about 90 minutes apart. Reduced to linear form, the nightly dream-chart has the shape of a wavy line. The crests are Stage 1 EEG's of light sleep during which (except for the first) we dream. The troughs are stages of deeper sleep from which we rebound into dreams. The sleeper does not always return to deepest sleep as the night goes on. He may descend only to Stage 2 or 3 and struggle back to dreams.

There are 4 or 5 dream periods during the night. These take about one-fifth of our sleep time. The cycle remains quite constant, from the end of one dream to the end of another, but the time span of successive dreaming periods becomes longer—from 10 minutes or less for the first, to half an hour or more for the last. First the news-reel, then the feature.

Such is the dream cycle of uninterrupted sleep, as constructed by researchers such as Dement, Fisher and Kleitman. It is generalized and idealized and cannot guarantee a dream every hour and a half. Interpretation and collection of data has its difficulties. Some dreamers insist that they have not been dreaming, but "thinking," and even deny with some bellicosity that they have been asleep, when the observer knows very well that they have been. We are as individual in sleep as in waking. One's personal dream cycle may not be a precise 90 minutes, but 100 or 110 minutes or something else. A night of little dreaming may be followed by a night of much dreaming to make up for it. Excessive intake of alcohol, and other factors, can suppress dreaming.

Yet there is quite substantial evidence that dreaming is a cyclic

Awake

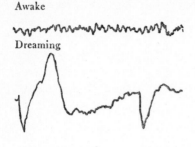

Dreaming

Top line shows electro-oculogram (eye movement traces) of a subject who is awake. Bottom line shows rapid eye movement (REM) characteristic of dreaming periods.

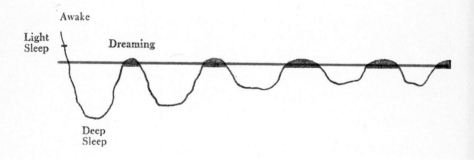

Rapid eye movements during sleep are thought to be concurrent with dreaming periods (solid black areas) occurring on emergence from deep sleep to lighter sleep. Four or five dreaming periods may occur during the night, separated by periods of dreamless sleep lasting about 90 minutes. Cycles of deep and lighter sleep alternate as the curved line suggests. The trough of sleep tends to become shallower as the night wears on. The first sleep of the night tends to be the deepest and the first dreaming period occurs on emerging from it.

phenomenon and that we invest about 20 per cent of our sleep in dreaming.

Relationships of age to the dream cycle have been studied to some extent by Charles Fisher of Mt. Sinai Hospital in New York City. In summary: A 2-year-old dreams about 30 per cent of his sleeping time. At age 5, dreaming decreases to 18.5 per cent of sleep and stays at that level through adolescence. The greatest proportion of dreaming time, about 25 per cent of sleep time, comes at about age 20. The dreamiest time of life may be the twenties, a conclusion the elderly may be disinclined to dispute. Dream time averages 18 per cent between ages 30 and 40 and a little less at 50. A 100-year-old woman who was observed one night spent only 13 per cent of her sleeping time in dreams. Most of these findings stem from observations of fairly small groups and need to be validated by further investigations.

The "as ifs" generated by dream studies are irresistibly alluring. It is "as if" we require rhythmic surcease from too-deep sleep, "as if" the brooding brain rallies the functions to withstand another descent into the dark trough of deep sleep. Is prolonged heavy sleep a hazard from which dreams defend us? The watchful brain, or "instinct," protects organisms in mysterious ways. Wild elephants do not lie down to sleep in the absence of companions that could help a sleep-drugged animal to rise. In a reclining position, the immense weight of an elephant's body, the distance of extremities from the heart, endanger circulation and elephants seem to know that if they stay recumbent too long they may pass into a sleep from which there is no returning. One may only assume that so universal a phenomenon as dreaming presumably serves some biological purpose.

Does Everybody Dream?

The consensus is that everybody dreams repeatedly every night. Neuro-physiologists, at least, have not turned up any exceptions. Ian Oswald writes, "We now have available evidence that normal people dream for about two hours or more every night." Yet hardly anybody could write a detailed two-hour scenario of his dreams the morning after. And many persons declare with utter honesty that they seldom dream or do not dream at all.

There is no real discrepancy. We forget our dreams with extraordinary rapidity. Most of the dream content is never recalled. Researchers commonly speak not of dreamers and non-dreamers, but of "recallers" and "non-recallers."

Various sorts of evidence indicate that non-recallers dream every night like everybody else, but suppress their dream memories or are less adept at remembering than the average dreamer (who at best remembers, most fleetingly, only a small fragment of his dreams). To determine whether a sleeper is actually dreaming, it is best to awaken him when objective criteria suggest that a dream is in progress or has just flickered to an end. When so awakened, non-recallers almost always say that they were dreaming, just as more accomplished dreamers do. But so rapid is the erasure of dreams that if the sleeper is awakened only 10 minutes or so after apparent termination of a dream he usually has no memory of it. It would seem that the dreams we remember most vividly are those we awaken from while action is in progress.

Subtle differences between recallers and non-recallers of dreams have been suggested tentatively by some investigators. Persons who say they seldom or never dream have about the same 4 or 5 nightly dreaming periods as others, but spend less time in them. They seem to get into and out of their dreams faster, and to do about one-fifth less dreaming than proficient dream-recallers. Some EEG evidence, as well as the behavior of subjects awakened from light sleep, intimates that the so-called non-dreamer has a more shallow level of sleep than average. Often he is the subject who, awakened from light sleep, claims that he hasn't been asleep at all but awake and thinking. Perhaps the non-recaller of dreams sleeps defensively and is well-suited for jobs, ranging from radar-scanning to babysitting, which put a premium on alertness.

The rapidity with which dreams are forgotten is no less astonishing than the enormous amount of fantasy that is never remembered. All but a tiny part of our dreams might as well never have transpired at all, as far as the conscious mind is concerned. We try to describe last night's dream at the breakfast table and grope for details that begin to elude us. Even the most vivid dream soon fades. Who can remember a dream of 10 or 20 or 30 years ago, unless it were written down at the time, embellished, and reinforced by conscious review? But real events of long ago have a tenacious grip on memory. Such "things" as the floor plan of one's childhood home, the furnishings of a bedroom, the kitchen cupboard stocked with molasses cookies, the bridge over which it was unlawful to drive horses faster than a walk, can be fished readily from memory's filing cabinet. The mysterious mechanisms of memory which might help to explain the evanescence of dreams have barely begun to come under sophisticated scrutiny.

Memory and Dreams

The classic dictum of Socrates, "Know Thyself," was in at least one respect applied indifferently to himself by the philosopher. Socrates proposed that the mind of man contains a block of wax which receives impressions of what we want to remember, like the imprint of a signet ring, and that we recall what is imprinted as long as the image lasts.

The idea that memory is some sort of physical imprint on the brain is ancient and persistent. The ball of wax theory has undergone many refinements. Prominent among modern theories is the concept of reverberating nerve circuits bearing the imprint of experience. In essence, the theory is that whatever is to become a memory causes impulses to travel over millions of intercommunicating brain cells, blazing a new trail in the nerve forest. The impulses reverberate long enough—or are soon reinforced by repetition, as by re-reading a passage to be memorized—to go around the circuit hundreds and thousands of times. When we remember, impulses take the route of least resistance, flashing over pathways from which the underbrush was scorched by the original experience. Such theories never explained specifically how memory mechanisms might work, and the nerve impulse as an exclusive model for all functions of the brain has been largely abandoned.

Current theories of memory stress the chemistry of cell nuclei, the transactions of macromolecules. To describe the theories more brashly than scientists do, memories are unique protein molecules which educated neurones continue to synthesize. The theories stem from advances in molecular biology during the past decade. Almost

69

every high school science student knows something about deoxyribonucleic acid (DNA), the long double-helix molecule which furnishes the molecular templates of the genetic code. Protein factories in the cell are located in ribosome particles, where amino acid residues are assembled to construct specific proteins under the direction of RNA (ribonucleic acid). DNA molecules, which if modified continue to reproduce the modifications, furnish the templates for RNA which controls protein synthesis.

Molecules capable of genetic coding may be capable of *memory coding* as well. In broad concept, this is what may happen: Excitation or use of a nerve cell causes a change in its RNA so that a unique new protein is synthesized and continues to be synthesized. Thereafter the cell responds to the same excitatory pattern which "printed" the structure of the new protein, but not to other patterns. The cell becomes reactivated functionally by stimuli that induced the protein alteration. And so we "remember."

The rapidity with which dreams are forgotten—indeed, never remembered at all—is of great interest to those concerned with the baffling mechanisms of memory. Perhaps the great bulk of our dream information fails to be processed into memory because it is too transient to leave an imprint on Socrates's updated ball of wax, the sites of protein synthesis. If, as a number of studies indicate, the nucleic acids of neurones can be changed by use and can perpetuate those changes to modify capacities such as memory, it is conceivable that desirable changes might some day be induced deliberately by pharmacological means. This could open the doorway to fantastic possibilities which at present, unfortunately, are only dreams.

Yet some progress has been made. Well-known experiments with a species of flatworm, Planaria, have yielded some astonishing findings. Lowly helminths though they are, flatworms can learn certain forms of behavior through training. Investigators thus have educated as well as illiterate flatworms available. It has been found that if an uneducated flatworm uses an educated flatworm for food—in fact, turns cannibal—something very remarkable happens. The uneducated flatworm acquires its victim's learned behavior. It has swallowed a ready-made education, presumably in the form of RNA that a trained but defunct colleague went to a lot of trouble to acquire. The education is chemically transferred. The stupid worm has learned without effort, and possibly has memories of events experienced by its victim. Memory is the basis of learning.

Studies of "sleep-learning" cited by Kleitman conclude that it is "impractical and probably impossible" to learn during sleep. A drug to make one's neural nucleic acids more receptive to faint impressions is quite visionary, but until something of the sort comes along, the hope that man can sleep and dream his way to mastery of anything that is learnable seems destined to remain the stuff that dreams are made of.

How Fast is a Dream?

"Instantaneous" dreams in which events of a lifetime flash through the mind in a few seconds are very popular in folklore. There is very little evidence that such high-velocity dreams occur, and considerable evidence that they do not.

Occasionally, an external stimulus incorporated into a dream furnishes a yardstick for measuring the duration of a dream. For instance, one subject dreamed that a doorbell rang, and he went to answer it, but before he reached the door the bell rang again. The observer had rung an electric bell and accidentally repeated the ring a short time later.

A more controlled way of estimating the duration of a dream employs EEG tracings to clock an apparent dreaming period during the light phase of sleep. The subject, awakened while the dream is fresh in his mind, describes the sequence of dream events and his narrative is taken down by a tape recorder. The time it would take the particular dream events to occur in real life can then be compared with the actual amount of dreaming time ticked off by the electroencephalograph.

The general finding is that the time course in dreams is much the same as in real life. And usually the dream is a continuous event, rather than a series of fragmentary experiences.

But a dream may be deceptively speeded by omission of some step in a sequence. One may dream of entering a skyscraper, and of events that occur in an office on the fiftieth floor, without remembering going up in an elevator. There is ample evidence of such

71

"telescoping." For example, one man dreamed of walking up a flight of stairs and then putting on his jacket in a cloakroom that he knew was located at the end of the upstairs hall. He could not remember having walked down this hall, and his eye-movement record confirmed that he had not.

Very speedy dreams might occur in a person of exceptional mental celerity, such as the phenomenal professor mentioned by Ian Oswald. Oswald made the acquaintance of Prof. A. C. Aitken of Edinburgh University, a most remarkable "lighting calculator." Aitken performed for Oswald a number of extraordinary feats of rapid calculation and many other related feats, "at the possibility of which I would previously have scoffed." Aitken claimed to be able to experience the whole of a passage of music, which would normally take half an hour, in the space of a half minute or less. A lightning calculator might have dreams of lightning speed, but the ordinary person who thinks at ordinary speed seems to dream at ordinary speed as well.

Tinted Dreams

Was last night's remembered dream a colorful experience? Did a dream-actress wear a red dress, or a stoplight turn green, or were there striking yellow draperies in a living room?

Most narratives of dreams remembered after normal awakenings make little spontaneous mention of color. Various studies have led to various opinions about the prevalence of color in dreams, ranging from general absence of color, to occasional recall of some vivid hue, to the frequent perception of color elements by dreaming painters, designers, and others to whom color is particularly significant in daily life.

More recent studies (e.g., Dement, Fisher, and associates) indicate that most persons, contrary to general belief, have dreams that contain some color elements. In such studies, subjects are awakened during period of rapid eye movements and asked to narrate dreams in progress before awakening into a tape recorder. Then the investigator inserts a few "colored" questions among other inquiries about the location, actors, etc. of the dream. Some mentions of color are spontaneous, others elicited. Of 87 dreams recalled in 100 awakenings, more than 70 per cent contained definite color elements and another 12.6 per cent were "vaguely colored."

Dreams in color may be the rule rather than the exception. Absence of *mention* of color in narratives of dreams is similar to its absence in reporting incidents of waking life. Color surrounds us always, but as a taken-for-granted background to which we rarely give rapt attention. We are more concerned with the meaning than the palette of circumstances, and color is gently put in its place among innumerable stimuli by the incessantly discriminating brain. A bright red dress is quite spectacular, but in the normal course of events we attend more closely, after initial dazzlement, to the possible "meaning" the girl who wears it may have for us, as we observe her demeanor and converse with her.

The unconscious softening of color stimuli in waking life is apparent when we view a color movie or color slide projected onto a screen. No matter how faithful the hues to the original scene, the projected image almost always seems more brilliant and garish than life. Handsome four-color reproductions of red, green, orange, and yellow vegetables in the food pages of magazines are more vibrant than the same vegetables on a cafeteria table.

Dreams are accepted as real when they occur, and the diminished color-recall is similar to that in waking life. It has been suggested that it is not the prevalence of color in dreams that needs explanation, but why strictly black-and-white dreams should ever occur.

Dreams Without Snoring

When a sleeper is snoring, he isn't dreaming. There may be occasional exceptions, but the rule is sufficiently reliable to encourage a tormented bedfellow to prod the snorer awake without fear of interrupting some fascinating dream. Snoring occurs during medium or deep sleep, but rarely during light sleep when eye motions are rapid (markers of a dreaming period).

Dreams may keep a sleeper too interested to snore, or his throat muscles may not be quite so relaxed as in deeper sleep. The first snore often occurs about 1½ hours after falling asleep, corresponding roughly to subsidence into deeper sleep after the first dreaming period of the night. One may surmise that a satisfactory brief dream has already been enjoyed by the sleeper by the time he begins to snore.

Snoring is harmless to the snorer, but is a form of sleep disturbance (see Chapter 5) which can be maddening to anyone within earshot, including occupants of an adjoining apartment with thin walls that transmit acoustical cannonadings.

Nightmares

Etymologically, the "mare" of a nightmare is not a horse but a fiend or incubus that in times gone by was supposed to oppress people during sleep. It is not easy to define a nightmare with precision or to draw a sharp line between a disturbing dream and a rousing nightmare. J. A. Hadfield has described nightmares as "anxiety dreams of such intensity that they completely overwhelm the personality; they give rise to exaggerated body sensations, of palpitation, sweating and suffocation . . . and fill us with such horror that we wake up in dread."

A dreadful dream in itself is not necessarily a nightmare. Accompanying somatic elements are usually mentioned—feeling of crushing weight on the chest, paralysis, suffocation. Such sensations could well arise from gaseous distention, pressing upon internal organs, and it is widely believed that digestive disturbances provoke nightmares. An indiscreet meal of cabbage and radishes, expanding against the diaphragm, might be felt in a dream as a giant sitting on one's chest. The concept that a nightmare is a sort of gas pain has plausibility, but there is little direct evidence. Whatever its causes, a nightmare is distinguished by its aura of terror.

The essence of a nightmare may not be troubled digestion, but terrifying realization that one cannot move when it is desperately necessary to move to escape danger. Frightening realization that one cannot move is a frequent but not universal component of nightmares. Several investigators have described this strange paralysis which the nightmare victim realizes at the very moment when he has a panic-stricken need to move and escape. There is brief inhibition of motor activity and the paralyzed dreamer, overwhelmed by unutterable terror he cannot flee from, wakes up screaming.

74

Treatment of the nightmare-prone is not standardized. A psycho-therapeutic approach which sometimes helps encourages the patient to describe his nightmare over and over again until it loses much of its frightening content.

Do Babies and Animals Dream?

At some time in life, everybody begins to dream. Do we start dreaming at the age of 1 year, or 2, or 3, or are we born with a capacity for dreaming which begins to operate at birth?

It is impractical to arouse a sleeping baby and make inquiry about his dreams, but objective methods of identifying dreaming periods in adults (EEGs and REMs) can be applied to infants. By such criteria, even newborn babies appear to dream. At least, during the first 2 weeks of life, the rapid eye movements character-istic of the dreaming state can be found during roughly 60 per cent of any 4-hour period. As the baby grows older, the proportion of his sleeping time spent in dream periods grows shorter. During the second half of his first year it runs about 35 per cent.

Not all researchers are convinced that newborn babies dream. One may wonder what a newborn dreams about, if anything. Fisher, who has done many experimental studies of dreaming in-volving infants and children, points out that the dreams of small babies are not necessarily visual. For example, they may dream of sustenance and hallucinate the sensation of sucking breast or bottle. At any rate, the only sucking they do while asleep occurs during the dreaming state. Three-year-old children awakened during a period of rapid eye movement give clear accounts of visual dreams. Younger children have not been questioned.

Whether or not very young babies dream in the adult sense, the mechanism for dreaming appears to be inborn and capable of rela-tively rapid maturation.

Do animals dream? Many observant pet owners incline to think so. Dogs often growl, bark, snap and twitch restlessly in their sleep, as if dreaming of the chase. Sleeping cats have periods of twitching movements of the limbs, whiskers and ears, different from periods of complete stillness. One enterprising student took photographs of a sleeping lion, showing Leo chewing and licking his lips as if

75

dreaming of a square meal of fortunately unknown composition.

Anecdotes about animal dreams are of course inconclusive. The subject is inarticulate. However, by implanting electrodes in regions of animal brains, more objective data about animal sleep and dreams can be obtained. A favorite animal for experimental studies of sleep is the cat, inventor of the cat-nap. Episodes of low voltage brain waves and rapid eye movements, characteristic of human dreaming, can be detected readily in cats. Presumably this in the cat's dream time, when it twitches its whiskers and makes slight movements as it does not in deeper sleep. There is some risk in assuming that seemingly identical phenomena in cats and men are actually identical, but it is an attractive working hypothesis that animals dream or do something very much like it.

The Dream Denied

If dreams are a necessary part of man's existence, and probably of other mammals as well, what miseries might befall a person who was kept from dreaming for a long time? The question was academic as long as the only way of depriving a person of dreams was to deprive him of total sleep. Objective ways of identifying dreaming periods, previously described, now make it possible for a tireless researcher to prohibit dreaming by arousing a hapless sleeper whenever he begins to dream. The most extensive and provocative dream deprivation studies have been reported by Dement and Fisher.

The investigative procedure is arduous, requiring volunteers to sleep under close supervision and electronic monitoring for 20 to 30 consecutive nights. The general plan is to get a subject's "baseline" by observing his individual sleep and dream rhythms during several nights of normal sleep, then to awaken him at every onset of dreaming during 5 consecutive nights, followed by as many "recovery" nights with dreaming permitted. In another phase of study, the sleeper was not awakened when dreaming, but during dreamless periods of deeper sleep.

Dream deprivation proved to be rather more disturbing than investigators anticipated. One subject "left the study in a flurry of obviously contrived excuses," and two others adamantly refused to have their dreams stolen after the fourth night. Lost dreams evidently produced formidable apprehensions.

General findings based on a limited number of volunteers were quite consistent. When people are deprived of dream time, they make powerful but unconscious efforts to make it up. Typically, on the first dream-deprivation night, a sleeper has to be awakened 6 or 7 times to deny him his dreams, and on the second night 10 or 12. By the fifth night, as many as 30 awakenings may be necessary to halt attempts to dream. During the first "recovery" night, when resumption of dreaming is permitted, the amount of dreaming increases about 50 per cent above normal and continues above normal for several nights. Evidently we make strenuous efforts to make up for lost dreams, as if to fill some shattering psychic vacuum.

During dream deprivation periods, subjects showed anxiety, irritability, and difficulty in concentrating. Several subjects developed marked increase in appetite, with weight gain—which might suggest, though reports do not mention it, that lavish dreamers are not disposed to obesity or that a drug to increase dreaming might be an effortless aid to reducing. Neither a compensatory increase in dreaming or anxiety symptoms appeared when the subjects were awakened only during the non-dreaming stages of sleep. But they did appear when a combination of drugs known to suppress dreaming (d-amphetamine and pentobarbital) was given. Symptoms followed the deprivation of dreams, not of sleep per se.

Dement concludes that "it is as though a pressure to dream builds up with the accruing dream deficit during successive dream-deprivation nights. . . . It is possible that if dream suppression were carried on long enough, a serious disruption of the personality would result."

One effort to determine how long a healthy young man could safely go without dreaming was very painful for all concerned. After six nights of dream deprivation the volunteer could no longer be awakened by loud noise or gentle shaking. He did not fall into the usual dreamless sleep which precedes dreaming. His attempts to dream were so continuous that he began to dream within 30 seconds of closing his eyes, and had to be disturbed over 200 times in the night. After 8 consecutive nights it was impossible to wake the

77

sleeper, and he began dreaming almost the instant he closed his eyes. It was impossible to deprive him of his dreams without depriving him entirely of sleep.

The implication is that we do not dream because we choose to, but because we have to, and that we can no more avoid dreaming than we can avoid digestion.

Where Dreams Begin

The cerebral cortex, the seat of thought and memory, the great roof brain which bulges man's brow so magnificently, seems not to hold the trigger which ignites dreams. Apparent dreaming periods, identified by objective markers, occur in animals from which the cerebral cortex has been removed. Similar dreaming periods have been noted in a human being whose cortex was not functioning. Supposed dreaming periods in newborn babies occur before the cortex has gained much worldly experience.

All of this suggests that dreams are generated subcortically, in the brain stem, the oldest part of the brain (see Chapter 3). If so, dreaming is associated with the most ancient brain centers which modulate vital functions.

Indeed, dreaming "acts as if" it were a primary physiological process, comparable to pacemaking activities of heart nodes or dialysis by the kidneys. No external stimulus or emotional tension or sensory information is needed to *start* a dreaming episode. The regular, repetitive occurrence of dreams indicates that the dream machine is self-starting. We cannot step on or disengage the starter button in normal sleep.

External stimuli and happenings of the day can undoubtedly affect events in a dream that was self-triggered, independently of those events. It is good fun to attempt to trace dream events to happenings of the preceding day. Very often one can identify some thought or event which reappeared in distorted fashion in a dream. This takes some of the mystery out of dreams. Most dreams seem to incorporate and build upon daily residues or impressions retained, consciously or unconsciously, of the day's happenings.

By dropping cold water on a dreamer's face, shining a light in his eyes, and ringing electric bells, researchers have corroborated that external stimuli sometimes are incorporated into dreams, but not so often as might be thought. From one-fourth to one-half of dreams recalled after such stimulation contain episodes of falling water or ringing telephones.

The cerebral cortex weaves images of a self-started dream into fantastic patterns. Researchers speak somewhat denigratively of cortical activity in dreams: "low cerebral vigilance . . . inefficient attention to data . . . content organized illogically . . . irrelevant images when the mind wanders . . . defective analysis . . . crude level of thinking." The moral censor is absent, or at least wayward. If such is the stuff that dreams are made of, the interpretation of dreams evidently depends on evidence furnished by rather low-grade thinking.

Dreams and Psychoanalysis

Psychoanalysis is conducted at clinical levels. Research reported in this chapter is pursued at neurophysiological levels and is concerned with mechanisms rather than the content of dreams. Such research has little relevance to insights into personality and character that psychologists and psychiatrists may glean from dream narratives. But some of the findings impinge obliquely upon suppositions and theories of dream interpretion.

For example, the rapidity with which dreams are forgotten makes it unnecessary to invoke "repression" to account for failure to recall most dream material. And the apparent fact that the overwhelming majority of dreams are never remembered suggests that the few that are recalled may not be representative samples.

Oswald points out that "when a patient reports his dreams to a psychotherapist each week, describing dream events which may have occupied a few minutes, he is describing only a very small fraction of his dreams of the week. Out of the patient's report, the therapist seizes on a few events which seem to him significant. When the therapist comes to publish his views about dreams, he describes only those selected few of the fractions of the patient's actual dream life which are relevant to his theme. . . . It has always been a major fault of such writers that they have failed to acknowledge the clear experimental evidence that recall is not really recall at all, not really a recon-

79

struction, but largely a construction at the time of attempted recall.

"We must be clear that what the patient tells the therapist can only relate to an insignificant fraction of his dream life and may be largely waking fantasy material. Such material may well serve to inform the experienced clinician about the patient's personality, but is not to be relied upon as evidence of what really happens during dream periods."

In his darkest view, dream narratives may not exemplify clever, subtle mental mechanisms but may be simply examples of sheer incompetence in thinking.

An ingenious experiment indicating that there's many a slip twixt the dream and its recall was carried out by R. M. Whitman and co-workers. Two patients who were undergoing psychoanalysis were awakened once or twice a night during dreaming periods, identified by EEG and REM techniques. The patients described their freshly recalled dreams to the experimenter. These narratives were later compared with the dream stories the patients told their psychiatrist. Some dreams told to the experimenter were not reported to the psychiatrist. Some dreams "recalled" for the psychiatrist were not told to the experimenter. There were many changes and deletions in particular dreams related to the psychiatrist, compared to the original stories told to the experimenter immediately after the dreams occurred. Particularly, elements to which the patient expected the analyst to react negatively were expunged. The report is wryly titled, "Which dream does the patient tell?"

Schizophrenia has been described, among hundreds of other descriptions, as a dream state persisting in waking life. One study of 5 borderline potentially schizophrenic patients showed that dream periods averaged 26.5 per cent of a night's sleep, compared to about 20 per cent in normal subjects. When psychotic patients have been deprived of sleep, and thus of dreams, they have reacted with intensified phychotic symptoms. The evident link between dream behavior and psychosis has suggested that increased dreaming might provide a kind of therapy for some psychotics. Decrease of excessive dreaming might benefit others. As of now, the rationale and the regimen have eluded investigators.

The Function of Dreams

Irresistible pressures to dream suggest that dreaming has some vital biological purpose. Even electroencephalographers are human enough to speculate on the functions of dreams, though they are usually careful to label speculation as such and to stress that "further study is needed."

There is a plethora of theories about the "purpose" of dreams. Some theories cancel each other—for example, the theory that dreams help us to wipe out a thousand useless memories of the day, vis-a-vis the theory that dreams help to fix memories. Freud held that dreams protect sleep. Occurrence of dreams during the light stage of sleep when the brain is nearly as alert as in the waking state may be an ancient pattern of protection to guard a sleep-drugged creature against becoming easy prey for enemies.

Or dreaming may be therapeutic insanity. Fisher remarks, "The dream is the normal psychosis and dreaming permits each and every one of us to be quietly and safely insane every night of our lives."

It may be erroneous to impute any vital function to dreams. Dreaming might be an acquired habit, an addiction, to which we return as unfailingly as a toper returns to his dram.

We can only be sure that we will dream tonight and in the morning will not remember a tenth or a hundredth of what happened. Kleitman has remarked irreverently that Hamlet's line, "to sleep, perchance to dream" should be revised to "perchance to recall *some* dreams."

THE RAVELL'D SLEAVE

Chapter 5

If sleep "knits up the ravell'd sleave of care," it is sometimes too brief or prolonged or disturbed to weave a restful garment. Some disorders of sleep (parasomnias) are so mild that patients hardly ever bother their doctors about them. Some are rarely encountered in a lifetime of practice. The most common complaint, often voiced with bitterness, is of insomnia, or what the patient judges to be insufficient sleep.

It is hard to imagine taking the history of a patient without asking, "How do you sleep?" Frequently the question is superfluous; the information is volunteered, volubly and profusely. At other times, close questioning is necessary to elicit information relevant to the patient's sleep habits. A narcoleptic patient who complains only of "always being tired" may have symptoms consistent with hypothyroidism, but amphetamines rather than thyroid substance would be proper medication. There is room for considerable diagnostic acumen in the re-weaving of sleaves ravell'd in rare and common ways.

Snoring

If one were permitted to choose an affliction to suffer from, snoring would be near the top of the list. It causes no health injury. It causes no discomfort to the patient, who seems to enjoy it hugely. The patient only knows of his affliction through hearsay evidence.

All the damage, which can be severe, is inflicted on others within earshot. "Earshot" may be the neighboring apartment in a modern thin-walled building.

Some 300 anti-snore gadgets have been registered in the U. S. Patent Office, and it may be assumed that most of them were devised by desperate inventors driven to feats of creativity by the stertors of others. Snore-fighting devices include orthodontic splints, tapes, chin straps to keep the mouth closed, and uncomfortable obstacles which, when rolled upon, nudge the snorer off his back. In the past, even surgery was resorted to, an heroic measure to which the snorer must have been urged by a grave threat to connubiality. Surgical amputation of the uvula and sclerosing injections into the soft palate are ineffective and have been abandoned.

The noise of snoring, not exactly the sound of music, is produced by vibrations in the soft palate and posterior faucial pillars. Vibration occurs when soft tissues of the mouth and throat come close to the throat lining. There must be a reservoir of air in the nasopharynx. Relative position of the tongue and soft palate is critical. Sleeping on the back tends to make the rear part of the tongue fall into favorable snoring position. But accomplished snorers can perform in other positions. Fischgold reports that he has seen, or auditioned, snoring in sleepers lying on the side.

The quality of snoring has an orchestral range from piccolo to French horn, and modulations of the gasp, wheeze, gurgle, whistle and sigh. Variations of style are produced by differences in size, density and elasticity of affected tissues, frequency of vibration, and force of airflow. Habituation of the snorer to his symphonies is remarkable; he almost never remembers snoring, even though he may occasionally be awakened by an especially vigorous snort. "Short snores" or snorts take place through the nose with the mouth open.

Snoring seems to be rare during periods of rapid eye movements indicative of dreaming. Elderly people are said to be most likely to snore, presumably because of lessened tissue tone, but the generalization has exceptions related to individual anatomy, nasal obstruction, and capacity for complete muscle relaxation. Sheldon states that cerebrotonics—tense, sensitive people with a preponderance of cerebral over muscular and visceral receptivities—virtually never snore and "typically cannot sleep within range of the sound of snoring." The cerebrotonic has poor sleep habits and is subject to insomnia, a worse affliction than snoring. Proficient snorers usually are good sleepers.

Snoring is often associated with mouthbreathing, and if predisposing conditions are treatable there is some hope of relief or improvement. Nasal polyps are readily removed, a deviated septum can be corrected, blockages associated with infections and allergies are treatable. There remains a large group of idiopathic snorers in whom the habit is almost impossible to break because it is expressed when cerebral inhibitory functions are dampened.

Snoring can obviously cause insomnia—in a bed-mate. Tactful questioning may reveal that an insomniac may be cured by sleeping in a separate room or using ear plugs or muffling devices.

Somniloquy

Talking during sleep (somniloquy) is hardly a sleep disorder unless it is associated with other conditions. Rare indeed is the patient who asks his doctor to cure him of talking in his sleep, although tangential questions, rooted in apprehensions that inadvertent mention of a name or event may disturb domestic felicity, are sometimes asked. Some patients secretly worry that they may tell the truth and nothing but the truth under anesthesia; the discreet surgeon hears nothing.

Numerous references to verbalizations occur in the literature, but for the most part these are sideline observations, incidental to the researcher's experiment. Somniloquies are rarely recorded. Schwartz recorded EEG features of a woman who awoke from a very deep stage of sleep and talked in a soft voice. She seemed to describe something like an hallucination: "a very small man clothed in gold and walking on a radiator." The EEG pattern corresponded to wakefulness, but in the morning she had no remembrance of talking. Oswald mentions the ludicrous verbal constructions of sleep-talk which "almost certainly indicates participation in dreams." Kleitman states that mumbling and distant talking can be heard at any EEG stage, not necessarily related to dreaming.

Vocalizations lasting 1 to 5 seconds are frequently concurrent with gross body movements, such as turning over to change position. Talking during sleep probably reflects briefly decreased depth of sleep, usually accompanying body movements. Sleep researchers seem to regard somniloquies as entertaining artifacts unworthy of studies in depth.

Sleepwalking

Popular belief that sleepwalkers cunningly avoid doing injury to themselves probably rests on tales of dangerous feats performed by somnambulists. Legends are improved by embroidery, but there are responsible accounts of hair-raising episodes that sleepwalkers have come through safely. Laughlin reported the case of a man who walked along the ledge of windows at a height of 12 stories and returned to bed without waking. Hazardous feats such as walking along the edge of a roof have been reported. Such feats, if performed at ground level, would be trifling; what is striking is the absence of fear which enables some sleepwalkers to attempt ventures they would be afraid to undertake if awake.

On the other hand, sleepwalkers sometimes injure themselves by falling out of windows, crashing against furniture and walking into walls. They may also inflict injury on others in exceptional instances. On February 17, 1961, an English jury at Essex Assizes accepted a defense plea that a homicidal act was committed during sleep. Sleepwalking is a potentially dangerous disturbance. Various reports give its incidence as 1 to 6 per cent of all sleep disturbances, but subjects tend to be selected in one way or another and the sleepwalkers who are too ashamed or too little perturbed to enlist themselves statistically are not known. The disturbance is frequent enough to be an occasional problem of the practicing physician and perhaps more frequently of pediatricians. Emotionally disturbed children are particularly liable to walk during sleep.

Is the sleepwalker asleep, or half-asleep, or awake? The only consensus is that sleepwalkers never remember their adventures. Amnesia is complete. The sleepwalker will withdraw from a pinprick but apparently will not understand what is said to him although his hearing is unimpaired. Review of the literature suggests that there are different types of sleepwalkers and that the symptom may be associated with a variety of disorders, but no rigid classifications have been made.

However, there are many descriptions of what might be called the typical or conventional sleepwalker. He can see and hear and avoid obstacles if he is in familiar surroundings. The stratagem of placing pans of cold water to awaken a sleepwalker who arises with intent to perambulate is likely to fail. He simply steps around them. His movements are slow, rather rigid, automaton-like, but he is dextrous enough to open doors and turn keys purposefully. His eyes are usually open but there is lack of facial expressiveness, as if emotions were cut off. If he speaks, his speech is usually incoherent and disconnected, as in somniloquy. Usually he does not answer when spoken to but he may obey commands and submit to being led back to bed.

This condition resembles bewitchment or enchantment, which may not be wide of the mark, since many psychiatrists describe sleepwalking as a dissociated mental state similar to hysterical trance. Amnesia and failure to recognize danger indicate that cortical function is low in sleepwalking. The condition may not be so much a disorder of sleep as a peculiar interruption of sleep when motor functions break through. This happens to some degree when gross body movements are made during normal sleep. The somnambulist may experience this motor breakthrough in extreme degree when cerebral vigilance is at a low point.

Who is prone to sleepwalk? Some authorities suspect a familial incidence. Clerici reports an incident concerning a husband, wife and 4 children. One night the entire family arose about 3 in the morning and gathered around a tea-table. One of the children in moving about upset a chair. Only then did the family awaken. Greater frequency of EEG abnormalities among sleepwalkers than in controls is mentioned in several studies. Pierce and Lipcon studied sleepwalkers in the armed services and compared them to controls. They found that sleepwalkers were much less emotionally stable and had significantly higher frequency of temper tantrums, nightmares, enuresis, and phobias in their histories.

Sleepwalking episodes may follow recent emotional upsets or be

86

preceded by a week or so of distressing dreams. Authorities agree that anxiety is a strong component of somnambulism. Anxiety in children is not always recognized. Homework, pressures (in the language of pedagogic psychology) to over-achieve or undo under-achievement, exciting pre-bedtime routines, may need correction if sleepwalking is a problem and indeed if it is not. In such circumstances an hypnotic may be valuable.

Pai's studies of 117 service men afflicted with sleepwalking and similar activity included 71 who broke down after severe battle stress and suffered acute anxiety states. The men shouted orders in their sleep, tossed about, jumped out of bed and attacked imaginary enemies with such violence that some men injured themselves by hitting walls or falling through windows. This was not "pure" sleepwalking; the men appeared to be in a state of terror, muscles tense, respiration rapid. Extreme anxiety evidently provoked violent talk as well as action, as if in re-enacting terrifying experiences. Another 17 men with chronic anxiety were more conventional sleepwalkers. They often talked in their sleep, but walked in their sleep only at intervals. Their anxieties were less intense and their sleepwalking more "typical"—quiet, slow, seemingly purposeless. They too sometimes fell out of windows.

Associations of sleepwalking with epilepsy, enuresis, psychoneurosis, hypoglycemia, and postencephalitic parkinsonism are mentioned in the literature. Published rationales of sleepwalking tend to be more psychiatric than physiologic. Military psychiatrists have unusual opportunities to evaluate somnambulism in adult age groups since the condition is medically disqualifying in the army because of the possibility of self injury.

Sours, Frumkin and Indermill studied 14 naval and marine somnambulists referred for psychiatric evaluation to the U. S. School of Aviation Medicine, Pensacola, Fla. These investigators present clinical and psychologic data which strongly suggest that somnambulism of late adolescents and adults is frequently a symptom of psychopathology indicating ego disorganization and severe regression. The entire group displayed signs of inadequate male identification, passive-dependent strivings, and conflicting feelings in regard to aggression and passivity which, the investigators believe, led to or aggravated latent homosexual impulses and fears. It was found that sleepwalking is predominantly a male disorder and that it is seldom seen in overtly homosexual patients of either sex.

Nothing in the literature supports the popular idea that it is extremely dangerous to awaken a sleepwalker lest some frightful disaster ensue. It may be more dangerous not to awaken him before he does some injury to himself or others.

Narcolepsy

There is nothing abnormal about a bored and replete person's falling asleep occasionally in an office chair or station waiting room. Frequent, irresistible, repeated "attacks" of sleep during the day are another matter. Narcolepsy is a sleep disorder on the side of excess. The condition is characterized by uncontrollable spells of sleep lasting minutes to hours, at times other than normal night-time sleep. Narcolepsy is sufficiently common to present a challenge to the physician. Some patients fall asleep repeatedly during the day, some complain only of excessive sleepiness and dullness, and some do not complain at all until a change in their routines, such as entering military service and having to stand guard duty, makes them realize that their repeated attacks of drowsiness are unusual.

In well-developed cases, patients may fall asleep in extraordinary circumstances mentioned by Yoss and Daly of the Mayo Clinic: "Many patients fall asleep while eating, talking with friends, walking down the street, or driving their cars. Stenographers may doze while taking dictation; businessmen may fall asleep during meetings of the board of directors. Patients have fallen asleep while watching baseball or football games. After waiting several months to obtain tickets to a musical comedy, one patient slept through the entire play. One physician-patient reported falling asleep while performing a major surgical operation."

Narcolepsy may occasionally be a sequel of encephalitis or a brain lesion pressing on the brain stem. Idiopathic narcolepsy is more common and occurs in perfectly healthy people who have no complaints other than that they are embarrassed, even endangered, and possibly in trouble with their employer because of uncontroll-able compulsion to sleep at the most inappropriate times. Narcolepsy usually begins rather early in life and persists for years.

"Attacks" are indistinguishable from normal sleep. EEG data are not significantly different from normal sleep. Most authorities agree that there is no causal association with epilepsy. Night sleep is usually normal and refreshing. As a rule, the narcoleptic awakes refreshed after an attack of untimely sleep but the peak of wakefulness does not last long and drowsiness supervenes. Frequency of attacks varies with individual patients; as many as 15 sleep-bouts a day have been reported. With it all, the patient with idiopathic narcolepsy does not look or act sick. Usually he or she is well-nourished, and may have a florid complexion.

Yoss and Daly comment that idiopathic narcolepsy is easily misdiagnosed as hypothyroidism in patients who only say they have no pep and are tired all the time. Failure to improve on thyroid may lead the physician to conclude that the patient has a neurotic fatigue state, but in the latter condition the complaint is of muscular or physical exhaustion rather than excessive sleepiness. Agrypnotic drugs such as the amphetamines are mainstays in treatment of narcolepsy.

What is the cause of idiopathic narcolepsy? Attempts to pinpoint a site of origin in the brain stem or cerebral cortex have been inconclusive. According to a large body of informed opinion, the condition may be constitutional or hereditary and reflect a "bell curve" of biological distribution. In this view, the narcoleptic spends more time than most people in the gray twilight between wakefulness and sleep. His basic level of vigilance is slightly lower than average and he dips more readily into episodes of sleep than a person of natively higher vigilance. Just as tallness or shortness in populations has a bell curve of distribution—there are about as many unusually tall as unusually short persons, and the majority of people cluster toward the top of ascending and descending lines of a curve between extremes—so may inherent levels of cerebral vigilance vary in the population. If so, rare narcoleptics may have their equally rare opposite numbers on the opposite side of the curve: exceptional people who get along with little sleep and dip into episodes of exaggerated wakefulness. Narcoleptic patients tend to fall asleep at times when a normal person's cerebral vigilance tends to fall; the narcoleptic response is exaggerated.

It is well known that pressures on the carotid sinuses can inhibit wakefulness. Stimulation of these triangular areas in the neck leads to drowsiness and sleep, with characteristic EEG-slowing. The ancients suspected that the carotid has some relation to sleep, for the artery's name derives from a Greek word meaning "heavy sleep." Several investigators have proposed that narcolepsy may be a disorder of persons who are peculiarly susceptible to accidental carotid sinus stimulation.

There is some tendency for narcolepsy to run in families and to affect heavy-set, athletic males. The patient's neck musculature and adipose tissue may be such that the most ordinary and inevitable everyday activities, such as turning the head, may exert pressures on hypersensitive carotid sinuses and cause drowsiness.

Cataplexy

Strange cataplectic attacks are usually but not always associated with narcolepsy. The attacks may develop months or years after onset of excessive sleepiness. Cataplexy is a condition of profound loss of muscle tone, sudden in occurrence. An attack is as startling to the beholder as the subject. A feeling of weakness, varying in degree, overwhelms the victim. There is flaccidity and paralysis of voluntary muscles. The victim's knees buckle. He may slump to the floor or ground "like a puppet with all the strings gone." A mild attack may cause only weakness and trembling.

During the attack the victim is conscious but is a mass of toneless muscle. Attacks are self-limited. Muscle control returns in a few seconds or a minute or two and the patient is none the worse for his experience. Sometimes the patient has sufficient warning so that he can sit or lie down and not fall. Sometimes a patient is able to overcome an attack by some special muscular effort he has learned to make. A nudge or touch by another person often terminates an attack, but it will subside of its own accord quite promptly. Few attacks last longer than 3 minutes and most are shorter.

Stimuli that trigger cataplectic attacks are extremely odd: laughter, anger, surprise, any stimulus with strong emotional component. Elation on completing a difficult task or scoring a victory may provoke an attack. One clinician reports that a patient slumped to the floor whenever she scored a strike in bowling; other patients have collapsed on the fairway after making an exceptionally long straight drive.

Laughter is the most common precipitant of an attack. A hearty belly laugh literally makes the patient "helpless with laughter"; this and other common phrases such as "speechless with anger" and "paralyzed with fear" suggest to some that cataplexy, like narcolepsy, is a normal reaction in exaggerated degree. Boredom and monotony favor narcolepsy; gaiety and excitement favor cataplexy.

Sleep Paralysis

A patient's first attack of sleep paralysis can be frightening enough to send him to his physician in a state of agitation. Normal persons occasionally have such attacks but narcoleptics more often experience them. The patient lies in bed, conscious but powerless to move. Often he has a terrifying feeling that he is unable to breathe. Attacks most often occur during drowsiness in the morning after waking from a night's sleep but they may also occur in the drowsy period of falling asleep. Attacks occur during light sleep. EEG patterns during attacks show rhythms of alternating drowsiness and wakefulness but no evidence of abnormal electric activity.

Initially, attacks may terrify but the patient soon learns that the paralysis is self-terminated or ends quickly if someone touches or speaks to him. There is some speculation that sleep paralysis is similar to a cataplectic attack that happens to occur while the patient is drowsing in bed. Laughter or other strong emotional stimuli provocative of cataplectic attacks do not seem to be involved in episodes of sleep paralysis, although it is conjecturable that emotions heightened by dreams could serve as triggers.

Hypnagogic Hallucinations

Visual and auditory hallucinations are commonly and normally experienced in the drifting phase between wakefulness and sleep. They somewhat resemble dreams, but are distinctive enough to warrant the term "hypnagogic hallucination" in the literature. Like dreams, they are rapidly forgotten and individuals may be little

91

aware of them unless they have special reason to attend to them. They are phenomena of the borderland of sleep, irrelevant images that appear when attention wanders. Hallucinations are common in persons undergoing sensory deprivation experiments, and much the same muffling of sensorial input prepares the way for the onset of sleep.

Form and intensity of hypnagogic hallucinations vary in individuals. Narcoleptics appear to have special facility for marshaling vivid hallucinations. Mothers may think they hear a child crying or a doorbell ringing. Patients have dozed while watching television and believed that they had witnessed the end of the program, only to become fully alert later and realize that the program was continuing. One may hear one's name spoken, or an unreal figure may materialize in the room.

Since the mind retains some contact with reality, or oscillates between sleep and the real world, hypnagogic hallucinations are generally "felt" to be different from dreams. Usually there is not the same sense of real participation as in dreams; a modicum of objectivity remains. But sharp distinctions are difficult to draw. Transitions from one to another level of consciousness can be very rapid. Hypnagogic hallucinations have been characterized by some investigators as "micro-dreams" which occur when the eyes are open and the subject indignantly denies that he was asleep.

Visions may take geometric forms, colored lines, bright points, floating lights, resembling the images produced if one presses firmly on the eyeball for a half minute or so. Faces, figures, landscapes and abstract shapes may be seen in hypnagogic hallucinations. How do such visions arise? The retina of the eye is spontaneously active and has an important role in maintaining the level of activity of the reticular formation during darkness. Visual sensations can emanate from the retina without any visual stimulus, and some theorists explain visions as false perceptions based on this activity. Against this is the apparent fact that visual and auditory hypnagogic images are like other "mental" images, responses which need not depend on sense-organ stimulation at all.

Hallucinations occur in psychoses, acute alcoholism, and other deplorable circumstances which tend to give the word a bad name.

Common hypnagogic hallucinations are quite respectable and appear to be among the factors coincidental with settling down to sleep and waking from it gracefully. Only in certain circumstances may it be hazardous to give rapt attention to vivid hallucinations.

Dangerous Drowsiness

If a tunnel were built under the English channel, what might be the effects on motorists driving 20 miles or so through a tube that enclosed them, shut out external stimuli, and made it impossible to escape rhythmically repeated monotonous stimuli through the course of the journey? Might the stroboscopic effect of tunnel lights, the purr of tires, the dull harmonics of mixed reverberations, the hypnotic effect of a white line stretching straight ahead as far as the eye can see to a pinpoint on which walls converge, lull some drivers into dangerous drowsiness? Accidents caused by drowsiness or falling asleep at the wheel occur on ordinary highways. Modern life creates many situations of work, travel, and operation of machinery in which sustained cerebral vigilance is essential to safety of the individual and of others.

Hazards of untimely sleepiness are recognized. Motorists are admonished to pull to the side of the road and take a nap when sleepy. But little scientific work has been done to discover definite criteria which might detect persons who are predisposed to sleep easily, so that they could be excluded from certain safety jobs in which they might be dangerous. Two French investigators, concerned with practical problems of choosing pilots and others responsible for safety measures in their jobs, have plowed some ground in this area. H. Gastaut and J. Bert of the Faculty of Medicine, Marseilles, reported some preliminary findings at a symposium on the nature of sleep; discussants, who were for the most part physiologists, contributed insights to a problem that all recognized to be of great importance.

Gastaut and Bert made electroencephalographic records of 156 subjects who were subjected to standardized visual and auditory stimuli under experimental conditions. Blockage of the alpha rhythm was a gauge of habituation to repetitive sensory stimuli. These investigators found that signs of sleep appeared most fre-

93

quently during periods of habituation to stimuli and that there is a positive correlation between the rapidity of habituation blocking the alpha rhythm and the appearance of signs of sleep. They suggest the possible identification by the EEG of individuals with a marked tendency to fall asleep through a mechanism of repetitive inhibition.

It is not merely a matter of identifying the least sleep-prone persons, but of recognizing conditions in which the human nervous system can function most vigilantly. Boredom and comfort notoriously invite sleep. Yet working conditions are often improved by providing a comfortable armchair and a silent place for the guardian of a post of safety. The sound of a clock, an air conditioner, or the rhythmic flashing of lights on a control panel, may add the sleep-inviting effect of repetitive sensory stimuli. Many people are confronted with repetitive situations where they have to remain alert although the situation is of great boredom to them.

Putting in a variety of stimuli seems to be important in maintaining wakefulness, but the meaning of the stimulus to the person is evidently important too. Some people are kept awake by a dripping tap, certainly a rhythmic stimulus. Visual and auditory hallucinations occur in experiments of total isolation from stimuli, and such studies in truck drivers have led to surprising and even terrifying conclusions, because the subjects attended to their hallucinations with great interest.

Investigators have repeatedly noted that high muscle tonus is characteristic of wakefulness and low tonus of sleep. No doubt some muscles are more important than others in maintaining, or reflecting, one's state of arousal and alertness. Nothing like a reliable muscle-index of proneness to sleep has been devised, but certain muscles of the ocular system control an activity that is easy to observe—the rate of blinking. "Good blinkers" may resist drowsiness more effectively than mediocre blinkers. Whether this might provide a handy way of identifying persons with an innate capacity for sustained high arousal is quite speculative, but one investigator has noted individual differences in the length of time taken in blinking. Lawson recorded the blinking-rates of subjects and noted the length of time in which the eye was covered. He found that in a "good blinker" the eye was covered about 40 per cent of the time. So a really good blinker driving a car for 100 miles drives about 40 miles with his eyes shut—but probably at a high level of arousal.

Kennedy and Travis, working in Boston, found that a thin muscle located over the eye begins to give out signals when drowsiness comes on. These investigators equipped truck drivers with devices for summating and integrating the action potentials from these muscles. When the potentials fall below a certain value, an arousal stimulus such as an electric bell or flashing light is triggered.

Capacity for sustained alertness is of course relative. Everybody at some time becomes overwhelmingly drowsy and sleep ensues. Psychologic as well as physiologic factors are important in sustaining alertness; there is no satisfactory physiologic definition of boredom. Methods of screening individuals for basal cerebral vigilance—a BCV comparable to a BMR—would be desirable whenever safety is involved, but the present status of the matter is well described by the line with which cautious investigators terminate their reports: "Further study is needed."

Insomnia

More has been written about insomnia than any other sleep disorder. Decent respect for the opinions of physicians requires that still another discussion of insomnia be temperate in citing a literature which embraces thousands of papers, some of them good somnifacients. The literature on insomnia burgeoned when ways of making sleep more comfortable began to come into general use. There were no bed springs until shortly before the Civil War. The rate of increase of insomnia has roughly paralleled an asserted increase in tensions, stresses and anxieties in the modern world, and has also paralleled a proliferation of measures to combat insomnia. Numerous writers state, though without documentation, that the U. S. is the most insomniac country in the world. However that may be, every physician knows that insomnia is a very common complaint in his practice and a symptom to be evaluated with care.

There is no arbitrary yardstick of insomnia in terms of "lost" sleep. The patient may merely complain that he "can't get to sleep," or is "always tired," or such vague information may be elicited in taking a case history. The "quality" of sleep, its depth or intermittence or duration, may be the focus of the patient's attention. Insomnia is like total deprivation of sleep; it differs only in degree. It is obvious from sleep-deprivation studies reported elsewhere in this book that no disaster need be feared from loss of a night's sleep. An occasional "bad night" is a universal experience of mankind, taken in stride by all but the most clamorous hypochondriac. Persistent insomnia is like a self-energizing mechanism that the patient is helpless to interrupt. Fear of the night, of bedtime, of anticipated insomnia may become predominant. Some insomniacs may be in actual despair from their sleeplessness, "tortured" by imagined dangers, suffering from indirect and psychologic results as well as direct results of lack of sleep.

Complaints of insomnia almost always originate with the patient unless he is hospitalized or otherwise under observation. Symptoms of prolonged insomnia are non-specific. The experienced eye may discern signs of fatigue, lack of concentration, deficient memory, incoordination, anorexia, irritability, and often a restless, apprehensive mien suggesting underlying fears.

On the other hand, there are patients who complain little or not at all about insomnia but who the physician suspects would probably benefit from a little more or a little better sleep. Insomnia is frequent among elderly people, and the common textbook statement that need for sleep diminishes with age has been seriously questioned (see page 31). Patients' subjective attitudes toward sleep vary with the values they assume it confers, the amount and quality they deem satisfactory, and the casual or distraught attention they give to it. Kingman states in an oft-quoted remark that "those who sleep 8 hours and believe that they need 10 consider themselves to be suffering just as much from insomnia as others who cannot get more than 4 or 5 hours of sleep but who would be satisfied with 6 or 7."

Varieties of Insomnia

The most innocuous form of insomnia afflicts poets who are despairingly sleepless for love of a maid who scorns them. Lyric insomnia lasts for a stanza or two and is cured by discovery of another woman.

Nomenclature and classification of other varieties of insomnia is somewhat confusing, doubtless because insomnia is not easily compartmented. Various authors use different terms and pigeonhole insomnia on a basis of cause, degree, acuteness or chronicity, and time of incidence. The physician recognizes various manifestations of insomnia which he sees in his practice, and may in good conscience accept any terminology or invent his own as he proceeds with practical matters of management.

Some authors distinguish between primary or essential insomnia, and secondary or symptomatic insomnia. Distinctions are rather ambiguous. Primary insomnia, implying unknown causality, may reflect hereditary predisposition of constitution and temperament. Secondary insomnia implies various organic or psychic circumstances which raise the threshold of wakefulness. Insomnia often accompanies pain and innumerable disorders which are primary targets of treatment.

The case of the patient who "can't sleep," but actually gets ample sleep, is labeled "pseudo-insomnia" by some writers. Usually it is futile to trap such a patient by records of actual sleep time furnished by a nurse or spouse as proof of deceit. The false complaint of sleeplessness serves some unconscious purpose of the patient, and the physician who is a sympathetic listener is in a good position to get to the bottom of matters in the background.

"Rational" insomnia disturbs most people at some time. The precipitating cause is evident and quite reasonable—a time of grief, shock, broken routine, extreme effort, great worry, which murders sleep. A philosophy of "this too shall pass" is sustaining, but an unaided patient may have difficulty in interrupting a pattern of sleeplessness that feeds upon and prolongs itself. An hypnotic may be invaluable in tiding the patient over a time of stress, shortening it, and assisting the return of normal sleep routines.

Initial or pre-dormitional insomnia is the most common type. This consists of difficulty in getting to sleep. Most clinicians agree that more patients complain of failure to fall asleep in a reasonable time than of broken sleep or too early awakening. The onset of sleep is delayed, and the patient's hours of wakefulness when everyone else is sleeping and everything is quiet may seem to him much longer than they in fact are. Oswald finds it easy to understand how an anxiously active mind can prevent the onset of sleep in a person who is already awake, on a basis of "excitatory corticofugal bombardment of the reticular formation." He concludes that the less common insomnias, manifested by frequent or early awakening from a sleep that is already present, remain a considerable challenge to research.

The patient who complains that he or she wakes in the middle of the night and can't get back to sleep with satisfying celerity may have what some authors call intermittent or broken insomnia. Others suggest that such patients may merely have more vivid remembrance of wakeful periods that everyone has during sleep. Benjamin Franklin evidently had this type of insomnia, though he did not dignify it by that name. He lived before insomnia was endemic, at a time when people took sleep for granted and did not brood much about its vagaries. Franklin had an eminently practical and inventive turn of mind and considerable knowledge of medicine, evidenced by his invention of a catheter and of bifocal spectacles. He believed that he woke prematurely after a few hours' sleep because his bed became too warm. He cured his "intermittent insomnia" by having two beds. When he woke up in the middle of the night, he moved to the second bed and fell asleep again between cool sheets.

Physicians may consider that the term "terminal insomnia" has morbid connotations. It refers to early-morning awakening that ends sleep too soon, or what the patient considers to be too soon. In some cases it may be that sleep has come to a natural end. Sleep can be viewed as a process of waking up. Some people who wake to alertness in the small hours see no sense in lying abed. They may get up and earn a reputation as oddballs who get half a day's work done before the countryside is astir. However, terminal insomnia is not necessarily insignificant. Patients with true depressions seem to be quite susceptible to premature awakening and they may lie awake most of the night.

An editorial in the British Medical Journal cites numerous

studies agreeing on the important point that depressed patients suffer from insomnia, and concludes: "The depressed patient finds insomnia one of his most unpleasant symptoms. . . It is important that this insomnia be effectively treated by means of hypnotics."

Anxiety and Insomnia

It would be soporific indeed to cite innumerable reports which link the most common forms of insomnia with anxieties, worries, tensions, fears, the rushing thoughts of a mind that can't slow down. It would also be presumptuous to dwell at length on such aspects since every physician is well aware of them, or to belabor the consensus that psychotherapy for common insomnia is seldom necessary and that general measures combined with the doctor's reassurance usually suffice. However, it may be of interest to give a fair sample of comment by many authors on psychic aspects of insomnia.

Recommendations that persons with active minds should reduce mental activity to a minimum an hour or so before retiring are abundant in the literature. It is doubtful that any physician has patients who would confess to having other than an active mind; recommendation that the fierce rate of mental activity be slowed before going to bed is sure to be flattering and may be therapeutic.

Mechanisms by which anxiety may fend off sleep are not entirely clear. An editorial in The Lancet comments that "epinephrine is one of the products released as a result of increased sympathetic stimulation, and it is easy to see how anxiety can cause wakefulness by an epinephrine-maintained activity of the reticular formation, and the anxious man cannot let his cerebral cortex rest." In anxiety, muscle tension is greater and sensory input from muscles diminishes the chance of sleep.

It is commonly stated that persons fatigued by physical effort sleep superbly well but that those with "psychasthenic fatigue" have difficulty in falling asleep although they may feel utterly exhausted. There seem to be no controlled studies of the matter. Some studies, however, have shown that laborers such as ditch-diggers who presumably burn fantastic numbers of calories in their work can be canny conservers of energy; they spend a good deal of time leaning on the shovel. On the other hand, a sedentary worker who is all tensed up, biting his nails, twitching in his chair, fighting his telephone, may spend more physical energy than he is given credit for.

Overwork, as an element of insomnia, may be peculiar to conscientious persons who won't let George do it, and who accept more responsibilities than they can handle without sacrificing relaxation or letdown time. They may have no particular anxieties but a great deal of irritability and fatigue from incessantly chewing at what they have bitten off. A timetable of the patient's activities, obtained in taking a case history, may reveal the situation and friendly persuasion by the physician may turn the patient to ways of moderation and better sleep.

Often a patient says, "I'm dead tired when I go to bed, but the more tired I am, the harder it is to get to sleep." Peculiar anxiety may arise from or be a part of morbid anticipation of insomnia. A term more often encountered in British than American literature is *agrypniaphobia,* "morbidly anxious preoccupation with the idea of sleeplessness." In Rooseveltian paraphrase, the only thing the insomniac has to fear is insomnia itself. Solomon, in a review of insomnia, has described the process: "During [wakeful] periods at night his rushing thoughts, emotionalism, anxieties, worries and fears take possession of him in more unrestrained fashion. Then come his worries over real or imagined dangers of insomnia. Being more unstable because of insomnia, he is inclined the following day to be more in the grip of his anxieties and fears. His worry about the lack of sleep leads to excessive interest in whether or not he will sleep well." He is in fair way of becoming an agrypniaphobe.

A rational way of breaking the vicious circle of insomnia-perpetuated insomnia is to help the patient get some sleep. "If hypnotics are not used for insomnia, one can never be sure that other measures will produce sleep," Solomon writes. "Therefore, without the employment of hypnotics, one cannot give any definite promise of sleep on any particular night. But with medication one is fortified and can assure the patient that with a sufficient dosage and with one or the other of the hypnotics or some combination of them, sleep can positively be obtained."

To prescribe is not always to have the prescription followed.

Esperanza F. Sarino, M.D.
PRIVATE LIBRARY
Epalroaito C. Sarino, M.D.

Strauss, author of a Refresher Course on Insomnia in the British Medical Journal, mentions another phobia often associated with agrypniaphobia: fear of hypnotic drugs. "The patient may be terrified of becoming dependent on such remedies and becoming a 'drug addict.' If hypnotic drugs are given, as they may well have to be in cases of this kind, they should be prescribed in full strength, as the anxiety arising out of fear of the drugs has to be overcome as an additional factor. A bad night in spite of hypnotic drugs (given in insufficient quantity) adds to the general agrypniaphobia." Strauss advises giving a sufficiently large dose to be sure of producing an effect, and of leaving the anxious type of patient with as little discretion as possible in the matter of dosage and administration.

Craig's similar comments are directed to fellow practitioners: "As a profession we are unduly timid of giving hypnotics and in consequence the public, as a whole, objects to them. Brought up as I was in the same attitude, long experience has taught me the folly of such an outlook. The chief objection, I gather, is fear of inducing a habit. Once more experience has taught me to be much more afraid of the effects of sleeplessness than of any danger of producing an addiction, a danger which is almost negligible."

There are, to be sure, other measures of wooing sleep than hypnotic drugs. Many—indeed, thousands—of rituals, gadgets, and panaceas have been advocated, and magazine articles entitled "How to Lick Insomnia" always have an audience. Self-treatment is common; the physician sees only the failures.

Seduction of Somnus

We prepare ourselves for sleep whether or not we regard predormital rituals as ploys to induce slumber. Usually we lie down and relax in a reasonably quiet dark room. This reduces sensory input; in the language of electrophysiology, alpha rhythms disappear, cortical inhibitory impulses quiet the nagging reticular formation, and sleep, like happiness, comes unseen. Such simple measures do not suffice for insomniacs, and even many ordinary run-of-the-mill sleepers must yearn for a little help in improving sleep, if one is to judge by the numberless rituals and refinements of equipment advocated for weary people with thoroughly aroused cortices.

The ancestral pile of leaves has given way to beds and mattresses which astonish the simple savage. Benefits of the proper bedspring and mattress in improving sleep have been extolled without general agreement as to what is "proper." A relatively hard mattress minimizes body-sagging in the middle of the bed and keeps the spine more straight, but the spine has several curves of its own and it is quite possible to sleep in a hammock or on a floor with a block of wood under the head, Japanese style. A sagging mattress and bedspring may discourage frequent body movements during sleep; too-frequent stirrings suggest decreased depth of sleep. Kleitman, who reviewed the matter, concluded that "it is all a matter of individual likes and dislikes and, except through suggestion, the type of mattress used has little if any influence on the 'quality' of sleep." Motor-driven beds which vibrate or undulate may suggest to some psycho-analysts an infant's yearning to be rocked to sleep, but repetition of rhythmic monotonous stimuli usually leads to drowsiness.

Some people may be too cold in bed, others—like Benjamin Franklin—too warm—and either discomfort may disturb sleep. At the same room temperature, some people sleep under a light cover or none at all, while others feel that happiness is a warm blanket. A cold bed or a heavy weight of blankets may keep the sleeper lying too long in one position and he may awake with sleep paralysis, a condition that is more common in winter than in summer.

Long debate about separate beds vs. the double bed has produced no unanimity of opinion. Separate beds obviously remove a possible irritant, the gyrations of a bedmate. Furniture manufacturers and some single-minded sleep counselors have nice things to say about separate beds, but some marriage counselors deplore them. The compromise of a "Dutch wife," a bolster under the covers, is irrelevant to the debate; it is a stratagem of the tropics to improve ventilation.

Eye masks and ear plugs shut out light and sounds. But some people cannot sleep without a night light, and others require inductive sounds which disarm the reticular formation or soothe the cortex. Innumerable phonograph records and tapes promise to deliver hypnotic sounds to the restless, including "white sound," a tonal medley something like a waterfall which some dentists use to obliterate a patient's awareness of pain when a burr bites into a cavity. The muted sound of voices from a radio, perhaps reminiscent of childhood goings-to-sleep when murmurs of the elders were heard from a distance, seems to help some people to go to sleep.

Personal rituals of infinite variety seem to be useful conditioning processes if the patient has faith in them. One person's warm bath may woo sleep and another's may deter it, depending in no little part on expectation. There is no physiologic reason why a food snack before going to bed should prevent sleep; the expected effects in a normally healthy person would be to the contrary. A heavy meal may cause barely perceptible discomfort, possibly enough to keep some people awake, but a common indignation of women is that the menfolk, after gorging themselves to the hilt on a holiday feast, repair to a sofa and are soon snoring while the distaffers busy themselves with kitchen chores. Some people who are told that an overloaded stomach keeps them awake go to the opposite extreme and are kept awake by hunger.

Of psychologic rituals for wooing sleep, "counting sheep" is most famous in legend, but long out of fashion among sophisticates. The goal is to bore the brain to sleep, and any number of measures, such as reading an exceptionally dull book, can be quite successful. One pyschoanalyst has modernized the sleep-counting ritual. He promises the onset of sleep after painting 3 imaginary figure 3's on an imaginary black wall with an imaginary brush and can of white paint. Rabelais tells a mildly Rabelaisan story concerning "some monks, who, oppressed with wakefulness, resolutely addressed themselves to prayer, and before they had concluded half a dozen aves, or paternosters, we forget which, they all fell asleep."

The verdict on gadgets and rituals for improving sleep seems to be *de gustibus*. What works, works, and is as unassailable as a preference for caviar over sauerkraut. The important point is that rituals and gadgets do not work dependably in true insomnia and can give little more than sporadic relief. The true insomniac cannot let his cortex rest by painting imaginary figure 3's. He or she is the very troubled patient who needs and deserves medical attention.

Chapter 6

THE
PHARMACOLOGY
OF SLEEP

Many chemical substances are capable of influencing the nervous system in directions of sleep or wakefulness. Precise metabolic maps of biochemical activities associated with states of arousal or drowsiness cannot yet be drawn. Too little is known of cellular physiology. Drugs cannot impart new functions to cells or tissues, but can only intensify, diminish, or leave alone functions that are integral to the cell. Some drugs of totally different chemical structure can have similar major actions but different secondary actions or side-effects. It is now recognized that enzymes are primary targets of drug action in many tissues, but knowledge of their role in modulating interactions of drugs and structures of the nervous system is scant. The pharmacology of sleep and wakefulness is complicated by what Goodman and Gilman call "the as yet unknown perversities of a machine evolved for learning and dreaming." EEG records have shed little light on truly basic neuropharmacology, but much of clinical and informational value has emerged and, in Brazier's words, "it remains a matter of astonishment that so many of the brain's secrets escape across the wall of the skull to electrodes fixed to the scalp of man."

Not all the chemical substances capable of modifying sleep and wakefulness are prescribed by physicians or consciously used as medication. Some—e.g., epinephrine, neurohormones, hormones of the pituitary-adrenocortical axis—are natural body chemicals which appear to be involved with rhythms of drowsiness and alertness in ill-defined ways. Large amounts of central nervous system stimulants or depressants are obtained or obtainable by the public from dietary sources. These seem so commonplace and unpharmaceutical, furnished as they are in forms other than tablets and capsules, that it may simply not occur to the patient to mention them as possible contributors to his symptoms.

Puzzling instances of sleeplessness or lethargy may sometimes be related to self treatment with proprietary medicines, to thrifty consumption of prescription drugs left over from some long-past illness, or from failure to follow the physician's dosage directions. The patient may fail to take his medication, or he may overdose himself grossly on the theory that if a little is good, a lot is better. These are challenges to the physician's perspicacity and tolerant inquisitorial skills. Sometimes a patient may suspect that something in his routines may affect his sleep. The most common guilt feelings concern coffee.

Caffeine and Other Xanthines

Caffeine, theobromine, and theophylline are xanthine derivatives. The latter is usually produced synthetically. The many clinical uses of xanthine derivatives are outside the province of this book. As a group, these drugs stimulate the central nervous system, cardiac muscle, the kidneys, and relax certain smooth muscle structures such as the bronchi and coronary arteries. The drugs differ in intensity of their actions on various structures, so desired response and minimal side action can be attained with proper selection. These drugs are relevant to a discussion of sleep because caffeine, and to a lesser degree theobromine, occur—in the range of therapeutic doses—in beverages that are consumed in huge amounts: coffee, tea, cocoa, and caffeinated soft drinks.

Caffeine stimulates all portions of the cortex. It gives a "lift" that allays fatigue, increases the ease of muscular contraction, quickens the heart rate, and facilitates sustained intellectual effort.

A therapeutic dose capable of producing such effects is about 150 to 250 mg., approximately the amount of caffeine contained in a cup or two of coffee or tea. Huge doses can stimulate the entire central nervous system, including the spinal cord. The toxic dose for man is so large that no deaths from caffeine overdosage have been reported. However, it is not possible to stimulate the nervous system continuously over long periods of time. Heightened nervous activity is followed by depression unless there are proper intervals of rest and sleep.

Martinek and Wolman, in a report issued by the Chemical Laboratory of the American Medical Association, analyzed the xanthine content of coffee, tea, and cocoa prepared according to manufacturer's direction on the label, and reported the following findings: The method of brewing a cup of coffee has no significant effect on the amount of caffeine extracted; extraction of the caffeine by any of the methods of preparation is virtually complete. Almost twice the amount of caffeine per cup can be obtained from the regular ground bean coffee as from the regular instant coffee. Caffeine content per cup prepared from the regular ground coffee bean is roughly three times that of the regular decaffeinated coffee and about four to eight times that of instant decaffeinated coffee. The potential caffeine content per cup prepared from bulk black tea is comparable to that from regular ground bean coffee, although, if prepared according to the label, about 65 per cent of the leaf's caffeine is extracted. There is about three-quarters the amount of caffeine in green tea as in black tea. Lower amounts of caffeine obtained with tea bags are the result of smaller amounts of tea used in each bag, as compared with amounts recommended for use on the label of the bulk teas. There is over twice as much theobromine in a cup of cocoa as there is caffeine in coffee or tea.

Theobromine is a very weak central stimulant. It occurs in association with caffeine. The caffeine content of a cup of cocoa may be as high as 50 mg.

The type of stimulation afforded by small amounts of caffeine is so physiologic that the consumer is usually unaware of it. Physicians are often faced with a decision as to whether they should deny coffee or tea to a patient troubled with insomnia. Recommendations of moderation, in all things, are unassailable. An uplifting cup of xanthine beverage taken in the morning should have little effect on the following night's sleep.

Kleitman found that substantial amounts of caffeine in the evening produced a consistent rise in body temperature and motility of sleepers, consistent with greater restlessness and near-awakening in sleep. Smaller doses, roughly equivalent to a cup or two of coffee, had no effect on temperature or motility.

But caffeine quite evidently produces varied degrees of stimulation in individuals. Physicians, not to mention laymen, hear different stories: "A cup of coffee at dinner keeps me awake for hours" or "I drink all the coffee I want and sleep like a log." Personal baselines of nervous system irritability surely underlie genuinely different reactions. The phlegmatic and the hypersensitive do not respond identically to the same stimuli; biologic variability is quite annoying to researchers, in that stimuli and drugs can be standardized but people can't. A simple trial and error experiment—giving up tea or coffee for a while to see what happens—should theoretically resolve the insomniac's caffeine worries, but irritability at what he has given up may add to the true insomniac's inability to let his cortex rest, and require a physician's counsel and medication.

Goodman and Gilman, who are authorities on the pharmacologic basis of therapeutics, evidently are men of tolerably well-buffered nervous system irritability, for they conclude: "The morning cup of coffee is so much a part of the American dietary that one seldom looks upon its consumption as a drug habit, and there is no evidence that the practice is in any way harmful. The feeling of well-being and the increased performance which it affords, although possibly obtained at the expense of decreased efficiency later in the day, are experiences which few individuals would care to give up."

Epinephrine

Epinephrine, the major active principle of the adrenal medulla, was the first hormone to be isolated in crystalline form. It has complex actions on the cardiovascular system, raises blood pressure, elevates blood sugar, and activates the pituitary-adrenocortical system. Such actions are consonant with states of alertness, and there is some evidence that epinephrine may be important for maintenance of wakefulness. However, it is not medically employed for that purpose. Injection of epinephrine does not exactly duplicate its neurohormonal role. It is a substance of much interest to students of mechanisms involved with sleep and wakefulness. In arousal responses, descending impulses from the brain stem bring about the release of adrenal hormones into the blood. It is thought that epinephrine acts on the reticular formation to bring an EEG picture of wakefulness. It has been shown that epinephrine is released into the circulation when the reticular formation is stimulated in regions that produce well-known arousal responses. Few investigators doubt that epinephrine is somehow involved with rhythms of sleep and wake, but few insights into the nature of sleep have resulted from relatively meager biochemical research.

Sympathomimetics

A large group of drugs called sympathomimetics have actions resembling the responses produced by stimulation of adrenergic nerves. Some are powerful central nervous system stimulants and may be prescribed to postpone fatigue and drowsiness temporarily. Some, prescribed for other purposes, may be an unsuspected cause of interference with sleep. Pathways of action are by no means crystal clear, but EEG records and other advanced techniques have yielded some clues about mechanisms of the brain concerned with sleep and wakefulness.

Ephedrine raises blood pressure, stimulates the heart muscle, constricts arterioles and relaxes smooth muscle of the bronchi. It is a potent stimulant of subcortical centers as well as the cerebral cortex. Its alerting, awakening action is useful in management of narcolepsy and cataplexy. Ephedrine and its analogues have membrane-shrinking actions and are components of various nasal medications. Ephedrine has been known to produce insomnia.

Amphetamine is the prototype of many structurally related drugs which affect various functions with somewhat different degrees of selectivity. As a class, the amphetamines are potent stimulators of higher nervous centers, and the popular term, "pep pills," has been indiscriminately applied to some of these agents. The most conspicuous results of oral doses are wakefulness, alertness, elevation of mood and lessened sense of fatigue. EEG shifts toward higher frequencies are similar to those which occur during alert attention.

The diminished sense of fatigue is generally thought to be subjective and central in origin. Variations of individual response may occur. Large doses are followed by fatigue and depression. These agents mobilize energies but do not replenish them. Doses too frequently repeated obliterate warning signals of fatigue and lead to collapse from ignoring the need for restorative sleep and rest. Over-large repetitious doses can lead to acute toxic effects.

Amphetamine-like agents are contained in the majority of compounds prescribed to suppress appetite and assist weight reduction. The presumed target is an appetite center in the hypothalamus, closely associated with wakefulness centers. Some complaints of insomnia may be voiced by patients who are taking an appetite-suppressing drug without the physician's knowledge. The question "What medicines are you taking?" adds to the tedium of history-taking but is often quite rewarding.

Wide-awakeness resulting from amphetamine-like drugs is thought to result from cortical stimulation, but may also result in part from excitation of the brain stem reticular activating and arousal systems. Bradley, who suggests that amphetamine produces arousal by an action on the reticular formation rather than on the cortex, notes that mechanisms of the brain involved with sleep and wakefulness are very susceptible to the actions of pharmacologic agents, not only the obvious hypnotic and stimulating drugs, but to hallucinogens which seem to interfere with the integration of sensory information. "As yet we do not know very much about the precise way in which these agents act, whether they are interfering with synaptic mechanisms, acting through biochemical mechanisms, or perhaps even on local cerebral circulation."

Specific answers to such questions about drug actions on the brain might be revealed, Bradley feels, by use of multi-barrelled electrodes for ionophoretic injection of substances close to the cell surface while recording electric potentials of the neurone.

Central Nervous System Depressants

What physician would like to continue his practice if morphine and anesthetics were unavailable? Central nervous system depressants are among the most valuable and widely used agents in the physician's armamentarium. As a group, their actions range from mild sedation to deep anesthesia. Narcotics produce analgesia accompanied by stupor; hypnotics produce sleep; sedatives produce calmness without sleep; anesthetics produce analgesia. This classification is convenient but arbitrary. There are many overlappings. It is quite possible to give large enough doses of some sedatives to cause anesthesia. The common denominator of this important group of chemically unrelated drugs is their capacity to produce various degrees of central nervous system depression. The present discussion is concerned with sleep phenomena and no effort is made to mention all the valuable depressant drugs the doctor has at his disposal or their important clinical applications.

Ethyl Alcohol

Beverage or ethyl alcohol has been called the oldest hypnotic. Indubitably it is the one that has rolled up the largest number of case histories, many of them totally uncontrolled. It is also a substance obtained from dietary or quasi-dietary sources by multitudes of people who might be surprised to know that they are ingesting a chemical with actions characteristic of general anesthetics. Were it not for the fact that doses sufficient to bring anesthesia are dangerously close to doses that cause respiratory collapse, ethyl alcohol would be a good general anesthetic.

The night cap or hot toddy is an old-fashioned remedy for insomnia, self-prescribed by the laity, some of whom are not particularly troubled about sleeplessness and a few of whom extend the therapy into daylight hours nominally devoted to wakefulness. Alcohol is a central nervous system depressant that simulates stimulation at some stage by dulling higher cortical centers of restraint and inhibition. Large amounts of alcohol depress the hypothalamic temperature-regulating center, and a heavy imbiber evidently sleeps cooler and more like a log during the early part of the night.

Kleitman gave diluted alcohol in amounts approximating 2

quarts of beer to a number of volunteers about an hour before they went to bed. "Needless to say, the subjects had no difficulty in falling asleep after alcohol." On other nights the same subjects drank an equal volume of water, to establish a control level. On the "alcohol nights," the sleepers were quieter than usual during the first half of the night and their temperatures were lower. They were more restless and their body temperatures rose during the second half of the night. Total mobility through the night was about the same with or without alcohol, but its distribution was somewhat different from control nights. Initially decreased movement apparently causes discomfort which increases mobility during the latter part of the night. If intoxication is so deep that few if any changes of position are made during the night, the sleeper is likely to have a sensation of stiffness and discomfort on awakening.

The action of alcohol on the brain is not entirely understood, but according to Himwich, who reviewed the physiology of alcohol, "it probably interferes with synaptic transmission, for the break in continuity between one neuron and the next is the most vulnerable point in the transmission of nerve impulse. . . . Moderate degrees of inebriation can take place without any measurable diminution of cerebral metabolic rate, although deep alcoholic coma is always associated with a marked decrease of brain metabolism. . . . The areas most deeply involved are those participating in a process starting in the cortex and gradually descending to envelop the entire brain, including the medulla."

Older Hypnotics

Opium derivatives have a very ancient history; synthetic and semi-synthetic agents have greatly expanded the physician's choice of narcotics. If sleeplessness is pain-related, an analgesic is customarily prescribed along with an hypnotic, but the use of opiates as hypnotics has been largely discontinued. Primarily, narcotics are prescribed for relief of pain; adjusted doses do not necessarily induce sleep. The addiction potential of narcotics is well recognized in our own century, as it was not always in the past. A great variety of chemically dissimilar, non-narcotic hypnotics is at the disposal of the medical profession. Some of them are new, the products of molecular manipulation designed to invite natural sleep dependably, with satisfactory speed, with a minimum of side effects and with absence of addiction potential. Some hypnotics have been around for years.

Bromide compounds depress the central nervous system through action of the bromide ion per se. It is thought that bromide substitutes for chloride in the extracellular environment and that nerve cells are peculiarly sensitive to this substitution, but it is possible that there is also some intracellular exchange. Sleep induced by bromide is not particularly deep or refreshing, compared to that produced by many other hypnotics, and there is considerable liability to "hangover." Bromide is eliminated very slowly from the body and continued use may result in cumulative poisoning or bromism. The drug is often obtainable without a physician's prescription, and continued self-treatment may lead to symptoms of bromide poisoning, of which mental disturbances are the most prominent.

Chloral hydrate, a chlorinated derivative of ethyl alcohol, is a century-old hypnotic. It has some notoriety as the ingredient of "knockout drops" or "Mickey Finns." It is quite irritating to an empty stomach and must be given well diluted to avoid nausea. Proper doses give relatively quick sedation and sleep occurs within the hour. Usually it is a quiet and deep sleep with little liability of hangover.

Paraldehyde is a liquid with a disagreeable taste and odor, not very suitable for ambulatory patients. It has special value in psychiatric states characterized by excitement, and is usually administered in hospital environments. It is among the most rapid-acting hypnotics, usually bringing sleep in 15 minutes with an ordinary dose. Usually the patient should be in bed when the drug is taken. The quality of sleep is much like that of natural sleep and after-effects are uncommon.

Barbiturates

The oldest barbiturate was introduced as barbital in 1903. In a span of a little over 60 years, the barbiturate family tree has grown luxuriantly and fruitfully. Barbiturates of varied chemical structure are important central nervous system depressants frequently prescribed by physicians. Their actions, depending on dosage and structure, range from mild sedation to surgical anesthesia. Some barbiturates have special uses as anti-convulsants and intravenous anesthetics. By far the most common use is as sedatives and hypnotics—what the public thinks of as "sleeping pills."

Barbituric acid, the parent molecule, is not a central depressant. Substitution of various radicals at positions on the molecule gives a great variety of barbituric acid derivatives (some 2,500 have been synthesized). Barbiturates familiar in medical practice usually have a name ending in "al."

Adequate oral dose of a barbiturate brings sleep in 15 minutes to an hour. It appears to be very much the same as natural sleep, subjectively and on the basis of EEG records which usually are the same as in the patient's normal sleep. Likelihood of "morning hangover" or dullness is thought by some clinicians to vary with the type of barbiturate employed. Special psychomotor performance tests have demonstrated that some physiologic impairment can be detected some hours after awakening even when there is no obvious hangover.

How do barbiturates work? A great deal of investigation has been expended on this question without elucidating finer mechanisms. The cerebral cortex and the reticular activating system are most sensitive to barbiturates but the drugs seem to act at all levels of the central nervous system. Barbiturates increase the threshold of response to sensory stimuli several fold and adequate doses markedly depress all spinal reflexes. Some experiments suggest that the drugs selectively inactivate the lower brain stem.

By whatever route, barbiturates muffle sensory input and depress cerebral arousal. There is convincing evidence that barbiturates stabilize the cell membrane of neurons in some way, elevating the threshold of sensitivity, and also prolong the time of recovery from excitation, but details of the mechanisms are not known.

Barbiturates produce a paradoxical reaction of excitement in some persons. Oswald, commenting on animal experiments which indicate that barbiturates dampen the responsiveness of the reticular formation to incoming impulses, brings up a question that often puzzles anesthetists: why may two people, one of whom is anxious and the other not, but with the same blood concentration of ether, differ greatly in the ease with which they lose consciousness? "We can now realize," Oswald explains, "that in the anxious person the reticular formation is subject to exciting impulses, presumably from the cortex, and to the action of epinephrine, which has effects opposite to that of the anesthetic."

There is tacit assumption that depressive effects of alcohol summate with, and possibly potentiate, those of barbiturates. Death from ordinary therapeutic dosage with barbiturates is practically unknown. Goodman and Gilman conclude that "the vast amount of clinical evidence available does not warrant the view that barbiturates differ from each other with respect to margins of safety." Acute barbiturate intoxication from gross overdosage, accidental or intentional, occurs occasionally and not infrequently makes headlines when it is the chosen means of a suicidal attempt. Some persons of marked psychic instability—"addiction prone" personalities —deliberately seek a degree of acute barbiturate intoxication and give sinister implications to drugs which are important in proper medical use. Chronic barbiturate intoxication may arise from development of tolerance to sedative action, leading to increased dosage, or from thrill-seeking abuse, and true addiction may result, with severe symptoms if the drugs are withdrawn abruptly from the addicted individual.

The margin of safety of barbiturates cannot be stated with certainty, other than that it is less than practitioners would desire. Individual reactions vary. Doses 5 to 10 times greater than the effective hypnotic dose can be expected to produce moderately severe poisoning. Severe and possibly fatal poisoning can result from doses 15 to 20 times greater than normal.

Nonbarbiturate Hypnotics

Nature provides the pharmacology of sleep which researchers scrutinize as through a glass darkly and fortunate men ignore by doing what comes naturally. But many thousands of people are temporarily or chronically unable to succumb promptly to Marlowe's "sweet harlot of the senses," and require the counsel and pharmacologic assistance that a physician can give them.

114

Disadvantages of the barbiturates, and the devastating effects of unrelieved insomnia upon the sufferer, have spurred researchers to seek the ideal hypnotic which at one swallow would give 8 hours of restful sleep and nothing else. The search for newer and better hypnotics may never end. But newer hypnotics such as methyprylon, non-alkaloidal and entirely unrelated to barbiturates, have won an important place in the judgment of physicians and the esteem of grateful patients. Clinically important as hypnotics are, they have other uses which are little recognized outside of the laboratory. They are useful tools to investigators who study the occult pharmacology of sleep.

Some day researchers may even discover the specific reasons why we need to go to sleep.

This Product Information Superceded
Attached Package Insert

NONBARBITURATE
NOLUDAR

METHYPRYLON, N.F.—*3,3-Diethyl-5-methyl-2,4-piperidinedione.*

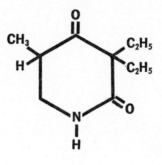

Barbituric Acid

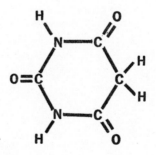

A Note About Sources

Anyone who essays to review the phenomenology of sleep is profoundly indebted to many workers in many disciplines. The difficulty of giving proper acknowledgment is suggested by the superb biblrography in Nathaniel Kleitman's book, *Sleep and Wakefulness,* which contains 4,337 entries. The compromise of putting reference numbers at the ends of multitudes of sentences to identify sources would give a gloss of scholarship, but at risk of imposing monotonous repetitive stimuli on readers who may have no desire to pursue facts into the stacks. The bibliography below, it is hoped, will identify names and sources of material in this book and lure the interested reader to original authors who have said it better.

References

1. Brauchi, J. T., and West, L. J. Sleep Deprivation. *J. A. M. A.,* 171:11, 1959.
2. Brazier, Mary A. B. The Effect of Drugs on the Electroencephalogram of Man. *Clin. Pharmacol. & Therapeutics,* 5:102, 1964.
3. ———. The Electrical Activity of the Nervous System. *Science,* 146: 1423, 1964.
4. Bremer, F. Neurophysiological Mechanisms in Cerebral Arousal, *Reference 49.*
5. Craig, Maurice. The Early Treatment of Mental Disorder in Mental Disease. *The Lancet, Lond., Extra Numbers No. 2,* Wakely & Sons, Chap. 41, p. 191.
6. Cruden, W. V. A Study of Wake; An Approach to the Problems of Insomnia. *The Lancet, Lond.,* 1:579, 1957.
7. Dell, P., Bonvallet, M., and Hugelin, A. Mechanisms of Reticular Deactivation. *Reference 49.*
8. Dement, William C. Experimental Studies of Dreaming. *Research Project Summaries, Public Health Serv. Pub. No. 1208,* U. S. Gov. Printing Office, Washington, D. C.
9. ———. The Effect of Dream Deprivation. *Science,* 131:1705, 1960.
10. Fabricant, Noah D. Snoring. *J. A. M. A.,* 175:265, 1961.
11. Fischgold, H., and Schwartz, Betty. A Clinical Electroencephalographic and Polygraphic Study of Sleep in the Human Adult. *Reference 49.*
12. Fisher, Charles. Further Experimental Studies of Dreaming. *Research Project Summaries, Public Health Serv. Pub. No. 1208,* U. S. Govt. Printing Office, Washington, D. C.
13. French, J. D. Brain Physiology and Modern Medicine. *Postgrad. Med.,* 27:559, 1960.
14. ———. The Reticular Formation. *Sci. American,* 196:5, 54, 1957.

15. Gastaut, H., and Bert, J. Electroencephalographic Detection of Sleep Induced by Repetitive Sensory Stimuli. *Reference 49.*
16. Goodman, Louis S., and Gilman, Alfred. The Pharmacological Basis of Therapeutics, 2nd ed. *The Macmillan Co.,* New York, 1955.
17. Himwich, Harold E. The Physiology of Alcohol. *J. A. M. A.,* 163:544, 1957.
18. Hyland, H. H. Disturbances of Sleep and Their Treatment. *Med. Clin. N. America,* 36:539, 1952.
19. Insomnia in Depression. Edit. *Brit. M. J.,* 5363:948, 1963.
20. Kahn, Edwin; Dement, William; Fisher, Charles; Barmack, Joseph E. Incidence of Color In Immediately Recalled Dreams. *Science,* 137:1054, 1962.
21. Kennedy, J. L., and Travis, R. C. Prediction of Speed of Performance by Muscle Action Potentials. *Science,* 105:410, 1947.
22. ————. Prediction and Control of Alertness. *J. Comp. Physiol. and Psychol.,* 41:203, 1948.
23. Kety, S. S. Sleep and the Energy Metabolism of the Brain. *Reference 49.*
24. Kleitman, Nathaniel. Sleep and Wakefulness, revised ed. U. of Chicago Press, 1963.
25. ————. Patterns of Dreaming. *Sci. American,* 203; 5, 82, 1960.
26. ————. Sleep. *Sci. American,* 187; 5, 34, 1952.
27. ————. The Evolutionary Theory of Sleep and Wakefulness. *Perspectives in Biol. and Med.,* 7:169, 1964.
28. Lewis, H. E. Sleep Patterns on a Polar Expedition. *Reference 49.*
29. Lovett Doust, J. W., and Schneider, Robert A. Studies on the Physiology of Awareness: Anoxia and the Levels of Sleep. Brit. M. J., 4756:449, 1952.
30. Magoun, H. W. The Waking Brain. *Charles C. Thomas, Publisher.* Springfield, Ill., 1964.
31. Martinek, Robert G., and Wolman, Walter. Xanthines, Tannins, and Sodium in Coffee, Tea and Cocoa. *J. A. M. A.,* 158:1030, 1955.
32. Olds, James. Pleasure Centers in the Brain. *Sci. American,* 195; 4, 105, 1956.
33. Oswald, Ian. Sleeping and Waking. *Elsevier Pub. Co.,* Amsterdam and New York, 1962.
34. Pai, M. N. Sleepwalking and Sleep Activities. *J. Ment. Sci.,* 92:756, 1946.
35. Pearl, Raymond J. The Rate of Living. *Alfred A. Knopf,* New York, 1928.
36. Raper, Howard Riley. Man Against Pain. *Prentice-Hall,* New York, 1945.
37. Rowland, Vernon. Conditioning and Brain Waves. *Sci. American,* 201; 2, 89, 1959.
38. Sheldon, W. H. The Varieties of Temperament. *Harper & Bros.,* New York and London, 1942.
39. Sherrington, Charles. Man on His Nature, 2nd ed. Cambridge U. Press, 1951.

40. Solomon, Meyer. Insomnia. *Med. Clin. N. America,* 29:178, 1945.
41. Sours, J. A.; Frumkin, P.; Indermill, R. R. Somnambulism: its Clinical Significance and Dynamic Meaning in Late Adolescence and Adulthood. *Arch. Gen. Psychiat.,* 9:400, 1963.
42. Strauss, E. B. Refresher Course for General Practitioners; Insomnia. *Brit. M. J.,* 4702:350, 1951.
43. Suomalainen, P. Hibernation and Sleep. *Reference 49.*
44. Tiller, Philip M., Jr. Bed Rest, Sleep and Symptoms; Study of Older Patients. *Ann. Int. M.,* 61:98, 1964.
45. Walter, W. Grey. The Electrical Activity of the Brain. *Sci. American,* 190; 6, 54, 1954.
46. ————. The Living Brain. *W. W. Norton & Co.,* New York, 1953.
47. Whitman, R. M.; Kramer, M.; Baldridge, B. Which Dream Does the Patient Tell. *Arch. Gen. Psychiat.,* 2:219, 1961.
48. Wilkinson, R. T. Effects of Sleep Deprivation on Performance and Muscle Tension. *Reference 49.*
49. Wolstenholme, G. E. W., and O'Connor, Maeve, eds. The Nature of Sleep, Ciba Foundation Symposium. *Little, Brown & Co.,* New York and Boston.
50. Yoss, Robert E., and Daly, David D. Narcolepsy. *Med. Clin. N. America,* 44:953, 1960.
51. Zuckerman, Solly. Hormones. *Sci. American,* 196; 3, 76, 1957.

INDEX

131

Esperanza F. Sarino, M.D.
PRIVATE LIBRARY
Epafrodito C. Sarino, M.D.